Instructor's Manual and Test Item File

to accompany

CASTRO • HUBER

MARINE BIOLOGY

Second Edition

Prepared by

Peter Castro
California State Polytechnic University

WCB McGraw-Hill

Boston, Massachusetts Burr Ridge, Illinois Dubuque, Iowa
Madison, Wisconsin New York, New York San Francisco, California St. Louis, Missouri

Instructor's Manual & Test Item File t/a MARINE BIOLOGY

Copyright © 1997 by The McGraw-Hill Companies, Inc. All rights reserved.

2 3 4 5 6 7 8 9 0 QPD/QPD 9 0 9 8 7

ISBN: 0-697-25688-X

Printed in the United States of America.

Contents

PREFACE

The *Instructor's Resource Manual* aims to give instructors suggestions and supplementary information that will make using the second edition of *Marine Biology* an even more rewarding and exciting experience for students and instructors alike.

The most significant points of each chapter are outlined in the chapter summary. In addition to the chapter contents, the summary briefly discusses the general strategy that was followed in meeting with the objectives of each chapter. Suggestions are given on how to present concepts to students and how to organize the material for class presentation. The listed audiovisual material and software should provide useful supplementary material. It has been updated and expanded. Oceans Online, of special note is a new resource, which serves the "marine community" and provides access to databases,online teleconferencing, libraries for marine related software, Internet and Usenet access, customer support services, and more. The Oceans Online system has been established to service professionals in oceanography, marine biology, geophysics, geology, engineering manufacturing, the Navy, the Coast Guard, civil maritime, maritime law and insurance, state and federal maritime, and university, collegiate and secondary schools. Oceans Online currently provides a LISTSERVE function for basic information on the system and will shortly be adding LISTSERVS for the major discussion areas. For an automated reply of topic listings send mail to: OCEANS@VBS.COM and in the subject line type: INDEX.

The resource manual also gives answers to the "Thought Questions" listed at the end of each chapter. These questions are intended to stimulate students' discussion of real problems. In some cases, particularly those involving conflicting issues, there is no "right" answer. They are ideal for class discussion.

The **Test Bank** contains a total of 455 multiple choice questions especially written for the second edition.

Instructors are urged to mention to students and use the several teaching and learning aids that are found throughout the book: the **Review Boxes**, **Key Concept Summaries**, **Do-It-Yourself Summary** questions, **Thought Questions**, and the **For Further Reading** references. These are explained in the Preface. The extensive **Glossary** and the **appendix illustrations** (units of measurements, world map where specific locations used through the book are indicated, and a map of the major coastal communities of North America that includes a useful list of field guides) should also be used as valuable resources.

It is my hope that this manual will make the teaching experience of using the second edition of *Marine Biology* easier and more enjoyable.

Transparencies

CHAPTER 1
THE SCIENCE OF MARINE BIOLOGY

Chapter Outline

The Science of Marine Biology
    The History of Marine Biology
        The *Challenger* Expedition
        The Growth of Marine Labs
    Marine Biology Today
The Scientific Method
    Observation: The Currency of Science
    Two Ways of Thinking
        Induction
        Deduction
    Testing Ideas
        Constructing the Hypothesis
        The Nature of Scientific Proof
        Testing the Hypothesis
        The Scientific Theory
    Limitations of the Scientific Method
Box: *John Steinbeck and Ed Ricketts*

Chapter Summary

Chapter 1 introduces students to the scope and nature of marine biology and its relevance in the modern world. The first half of the chapter describes the science of marine biology by sketching its history and by describing the many roles marine biology plays in modern science and technology. We highlight the fact that the study of life in the oceans now involves specialists from many disciplines as well as a wide range of tools and techniques. The box on Steinbeck and Ricketts puts a human face on marine biology.

The second half of the chapter emphasizes the scientific nature of modern marine biology by briefly discussing the nature of science and the scientific method, which is essential to understanding science. We outline its key components, its application to the real world, and its limitations. We feel the discussion of this material is essential to understanding science, most especially among non-science majors.

The inclusion of the scientific method in a marine biology text is an innovative idea necessitated by the general education requirements that have been implemented by many institutions. The chapter, however, is written in a plain, unassuming style and profusely illustrated in order to make the concept of science less intimidating to non-science students. It can be assigned to be read independently at the start of the course. The main objective of this section is to introduce students to the meaning and significance of the *science* of marine biology.

Audiovisual Material

Videos and Films:

1. Oceans (VHS, 55 min., color; Ambrose Video Publishing, 1290 Avenue of the Americas, New York, NY 10104; (800) 526-4663). An introduction to the marine environment. From The Living Planet series.

2. Life from the Sea (VHS, 60 min., color; Ambrose Video Publishing, 1290. Avenue of the Americas, New York, NY 10104; (800) 526-4663). An introduction of life in the marine world. From The Miracle Planet series.

3. Oceanography (VHS, 23 min., color; Films for the Humanities & Sciences, P.O. Box 2053, Princeton, NJ 08543; (800)257-5126). A general introduction to physical and living factors in the oceans.

4. The Dogwhelk: A Study in Adaptation (VHS, 15 min., color; Films for the Humanities and Sciences, P.O. Box 2053, Princeton, NJ 08543-2053; (800) 257-5126). From the Experiment: Biology series. Compares characteristics of two populations of dogwhelks living under different conditions and allows students to deduce reasons for observed differences.

Filmstrip:

Scientific Method (21-slide set, filmstrip; Educational Images, P.O. Box 3456, Elmira, NY 14905; (800) 527-4264).

Software

Scientific Method (Apple; Educational Images, P.O. Box 3456, Elmira, NY 14905; (800) 527-4264). Allows the student to use the steps of the scientific method by solving a problem.

Answers to Thought Questions

1. Nearly all of the major advances in marine biology have come in the last 200 years. What do you think are the reasons for this?

Reasons include increased mobility due to advances in the means of transportation (faster ships, planes), methodology (sampling equipment, microscopes, scuba, satellites, etc.), developments and discoveries in biology and other fields of science that have stimulated further research in the marine environment (theories of evolution, plate tectonics, etc.), improved educational opportunities and facilities.

2. In this chapter it was explained that the statement "There are mermaids in the ocean" is not a valid scientific hypothesis. Can the same be said of the statement "There are no mermaids in the ocean"? Why?

Yes, it is a valid scientific hypothesis because it can be falsified if a mermaid is found. No scientific hypothesis can be proven so this does not mean it is not a scientific hypothesis. So far all attempts to falsify this hypothesis have failed: no one has found a mermaid. Thus, the hypothesis is accepted as true, though not proven.

3. Imagine that you are a marine biologist and you notice that a certain type of crab tends to be considerably larger in a local bay than the same type of crab is in the waters outside the bay. What hypotheses might account for this difference? How would you go about testing these hypotheses?

Let students' imagination roam free, even if they may not know the limitations and constrains of experimental work! It's a great way to stimulate their imagination and desire to learn. One possible hypothesis: "Crabs outside the bay are smaller because wave action outside the bay is stronger than inside the bay." We can reject it if some of these smaller crabs are moved inside the bay, placed in a cage that allows food to move in (as well as smaller crabs from inside the bay placed in identical cages), and all are checked and their size compared after a reasonable period of time. Remember a control experiment: crabs from outside and inside the bay placed in identical cages outside the bay. This hypothesis is rejected if size difference remains when all experimental populations are compared. Other possible hypotheses: differences due to food, predators, parasites, type of substrate, temperature, depth, etc. Students should be advised not to despair if they cannot come up with too many possible hypothesis—these factors will be discussed in successive chapters, particularly 9, 10, and 12.

4. Many species of whale have been hunted to the brink of extinction. Many people think that we do not have the right to kill whales and that all whaling should cease. On the other hand, in many cultures whales have been hunted for centuries and still have great cultural importance. People from such cultures argue that limited whaling should be allowed to continue. What is the role that science can play in deciding who is right? What questions cannot be answered by science?

Science can provide evidence of the role whales play in the marine environment, factors related to the maintenance of biodiversity in our planet such as food for some predators (especially young whales), place to live for some parasites and commensals, and potential control on the population size of their prey (additional information on the biology of whales is given in Chapters 8 and 9). Science, however, cannot provide answers concerning the value of the enjoyment people get by observing (or listening to) whales, as well of their importance in terms of food and source of various materials to some cultures. Science can help us decide, however, who benefits the most.

CHAPTER 2
THE SEA FLOOR

Chapter Outline

Chapter Summary

The chapter summarizes the basic aspects of the geology of the sea floor and points out its relevance to marine biology. It includes numerous up-to-date maps and illustrations that are especially designed to serve as teaching aids.

The basic structural features of the ocean basins and the earth are briefly described first. This material introduces the student to a more detailed discussion of the origin of the ocean basins and the theory of plate tectonics. Information is organized in an easy-to-follow progression: early evidence for continental drift, the discovery and significance of the mid-ocean ridges, the creation of the sea floor, and, as a conclusion, a portrait of plate tectonics—the mechanisms that explains it all. Plate tectonics is then used to explain features such as trenches, island arcs, and faults. The box on the origin of the Hawaiian Islands further illustrates the consequences of plate tectonics.

The discussion of plate tectonics is followed by a description of the geologic history of the earth. It covers material that is relevant to current concerns about climate change. Integrated into this discussion is an introduction to the basic types of marine sediments. The chapter concludes with an outline of the geologic provinces of the ocean, which includes an explanation of active and passive continental margins. This section highlights hydrothermal vents, the deep-sea hot springs that serve as home to a most fascinating type of marine life.

The relationships between the material covered in Chapter 2 and the discussion of various aspects of life in the sea is reviewed and further integrated throughout the book by means of marginal review notes.

Audiovisual Material
Videos and Films:
1. Spreading Oceans (VHS, 16 mm; 24 min., color; Media Guild, 11722 Sorrento Valley Road, San Diego, CA 92121; (619) 755-9191). Plate tectonics and the origin of ocean basins.
2. Plate Tectonics—The Puzzle of Continents (videodisc; Media Design Associates, P.O. Box 3189, Boulder, CO 80307-3189; (800) 228-8854). The fundamental principles of plate tectonics.
3. Continental Drift and Plate Tectonics (VHS, 16 mm; 18 min., color; Phoenix/BFA Films and Video, 470 Park Ave. S., New York, NY 10016). An explanation of the theory of plate tectonics.
4. The Building of the Earth (VHS, 16 mm; 55 min., color; Ambrose Video Publishing, 1290 Avenue of the Americas, New York, NY 10104; (800) 256-4663). The forces involved in the formation of the earth and in continental drift. From The Living Planet series.
5. Continents Adrift—A Study of Scientific Method (16 mm, 15 min., color; American Educational Films, 3807 Dickerson Road, Nashville, TN 20036). Examines the scientific methodologies connected with the development of the theory of plate tectonics and continental drift.
6. Volcano—Birth of a Mountain (16 mm, 24 min., color; Encyclopedia Britannica, 310 S. Michigan Ave., Chicago, IL 60604; (312) 321-7105). The birth and growth of volcanoes in the Hawaiian Islands.

Slides and Filmstrips:
1. Plate Tectonics and the Spreading Sea Floor (20-slide set; Educational Images, P.O. Box 3456, Elmira, NY 14905; (800) 527-4264).
2. Sea-Floor Spreading (10-slide set, filmstrip; Educational Images, P.O. Box 3456, Elmira, NY 14905; (800) 527-4264).
3. Submarine Topography (15-slide set, filmstrip; Educational Images, P.O. Box 3456, Elmira, NY 14905; (800) 527-4264).
4. Deep-Sea Sediments (10-slide set, filmstrip; Educational Images, P.O. Box 3456, Elmira, NY 14905; (800) 527-4264).

Software
Plate Tectonics (Apple, IBM; Educational Images, P.O. Box 3456, Elmira, NY 14905; (800) 527-4264). An explanation of continental drift and sea-floor spreading.

Answers to Thought Questions
1. The process of plate tectonics is occurring today in the same way as in the past. Can you project future positions of the continents by looking at a map of their present positions and the positions of the mid-ocean rides (see figure 2.11)?

North and South America will be farther west toward the Pacific, Europe and Asia farther southeast, Australia farther northeast, and Africa farther east. The Pacific is therefore expected to be narrower and the Atlantic wider. The map in figure 2.11 actually indicates the direction of plate movement but it's better if students deduce these movements by the location of the mid-ocean ridges as indicated in figure 2.7a.

2. Why are most oceanic trenches found in the Pacific Ocean?

The Pacific Ocean is shrinking and plates are descending below surrounding plates along its edges, hence the creation of trenches.

3. Scientists who study forms of marine life that lived more than approximately 200 million years ago usually have to obtain fossils not from the sea floor, but from areas that were once undersea and have been uplifted onto the continents. Why do you think this is?

Part of was the sea floor at that time is now above the sea level.

4. What are some of the major pieces of evidence for the theory of plate tectonics? How does the theory explain these observations?

Evidence includes the fitting together of the coasts of the continents on the opposite sides of the Atlantic

Ocean, the similarity of geologic formations and fossils found on the opposite sides, a geologically active mid-ocean ridge running along the central Atlantic between the opposite coasts, bottom sediments that get thicker the farther one travels from the ridge, and rocks on the sea floor on one side of the ridge show magnetic bands that are mirror images of rocks found on the opposite side of the ridge. All of these observations are explained by sea-floor spreading from the mid-ocean ridge.

CHAPTER 3
CHEMICAL AND PHYSICAL FEATURES OF THE WORLD OCEAN

Chapter Outline
The Waters of the Ocean
  The Unique Nature of Pure Water
    The States of Water
    Heat and Water
    Water as a Solvent
  Seawater
    Salt Composition
    Salinity, Temperature, and Density
    Dissolved Gases
    Transparency
    Pressure
Motion in the Ocean
  Surface Circulation
    The Coriolis Effect
    Wind Patterns
    Surface Currents
  Waves
  Tides
    Why Are There Tides?
    Tides in the Real World
Vertical Motion and the Three-Layer Ocean
  Stability and Overturn
  The Three-Layer Ocean
Box: *Tall Ships and Surface Currents*
Box: *Waves That Kill*

Chapter Summary
Chapter 3 outlines the basic chemical and physical characteristics of the ocean, stressing their relevance to the distribution of life in the marine environment.

The basic chemical and physical characteristics of water are first discussed, followed by those of seawater. Student interest is sustained by photographs and illustrations that point out how marine scientists measure various chemical and physical parameters. The rest of the chapter discusses motion in the ocean: surface circulation, waves, tides, and vertical motion. We use a unique flip-the-pages illustration to explain how the rotation of the earth and moon affects the formation of tides, a process very hard to explain and understand using the conventional static illustrations. Two boxes demonstrates the practical relevance of understanding ocean currents and waves.

As in Chapter 2, the most important elements of this material is integrated with other chapters by means of marginal review notes. Furthermore, some material related to the chemical and physical characteristics of the ocean is covered in chapters devoted to particular marine environments: wave refraction in Chapter 10, estuarine circulation in Chapter 11, upwelling in Chapter 14, and deep circulation and the oxygen minimum layer in Chapter 15. This will further demonstrate students of the relevance of these factors to marine life.

Audiovisual Material
Videos and Films:
1. Nature of Sea Water (16 mm, 18 min., color; Graphic Films, 3341 Cahuenga Blvd. W., Los Angeles, CA 90028). The basic physical and chemical characteristics of seawater.

2. <u>Waves</u> <u>on</u> <u>Water</u> (VHS, 16 mm; 16 min., color; Encyclopedia Britannica, 310 S. Michigan Ave., Chicago, IL 60604; (312) 321-7105). A simple explanation of ocean waves.
3. <u>Waves</u> <u>Across</u> <u>the</u> <u>Pacific</u> (16 mm, 32 min., color; CRM Films, 2233 Faraday Ave., Carlsbad, CA 92008; (619) 431-9800). The nature of ocean waves in the north Pacific.
4. <u>Tides</u> <u>of the</u> <u>Ocean</u> (16 mm, 17 min., color; Academy Films, P.O. Box 3414, Orange, CA 92665). A basic explanation of ocean tides using animation.
5. <u>Water</u> <u>Masses</u> <u>of the</u> <u>Ocean</u> (16 mm, 26 min., color; BBC TV, 630 Fifth Ave., New York, NY 10020). The dynamics of the major water masses.
6. <u>Adrift</u> <u>on</u> <u>the</u> <u>Gulf</u> <u>Stream</u> (VHS, 58 min., color; WGBH TV, 125 Western Ave., Boston, MA 02134; (800)-828-9424). The study of the Gulf Stream by using different types of techniques. From the Nova series.

Slides and Filmstrips:
1. <u>Origin</u> <u>and</u> <u>Composition</u> <u>of</u> <u>Seawater</u> (10-slide set, filmstrip; Educational Images, P.O. Box 3456, Elmira, NY 14905; (800) 527-4264).
2. <u>Salinity,</u> <u>Temperature</u> <u>and</u> <u>Density</u> (20-slide set, filmstrip; Educational Images, P.O. Box 3456, Elmira, NY 14905; (800) 527-4264).
3. <u>Circulation</u> <u>of the</u> <u>World</u> <u>Ocean</u> (10-slide set, filmstrip; Educational Images, P.O. Box 3456, Elmira, NY 14905; (800) 527-4264).
4. <u>Waves</u> <u>and</u> <u>Tides</u> (15-slide set, filmstrip; Educational Images, P.O. Box 3456, Elmira, NY 14905; (800) 527-4264).
5. <u>The</u> <u>Tides</u> (20-slide set, filmstrip; Educational Images, P.O. Box 3456, Elmira, NY 14905; (800) 527-4264).

Software
<u>Ocean</u> <u>Tides</u> <u>and</u> <u>Currents</u> (Apple; Educational Images, P.O. Box 3456, Elmira, NY 14905; (800) 527-4264). Factors that   generate tides and surface currents.

Answers **to** **Thought** **Questions**
1. The winter of 1984–85 was particularly cold in Europe. The northern part of the Black Sea, which lies between the Ukraine, Russia, and Turkey, froze, which is rare in the normally mild climate. The Adriatic Sea, located to the east, had just as cold a winter but never froze. The Black Sea has an unusually low salinity of about 18°/$_{oo}$. What would you guess about the salinity of the Adriatic?
The salinity of the Adriatic Sea has to be higher. It actually varies between 38–39°/$_{oo}$ in the south to 33–25°/$_{oo}$ in the north.
2. Just for the fun of it, someone walking along the shore in Beaufort, South Carolina, throws a bottle with a message in it into the sea. Some time later, someone in Perth, on the west coast of Australia, finds the bottle. Referring to Appendix C of this book or figure 3.20, can you trace the path the bottle probably took?
The most probably route is: Gulf Stream, Canary Current to the Equator, South Equatorial Current, Brazil Current along the east coast of South America, Antarctic Circumpolar Current, and finally north along the west coast of Australia.
3. If you owned a seaside home and a bad storm brought heavy winds and high surf to your coastline, would you prefer it to be during new moon or a quarter moon? Why?
A storm during a quarter moon would be less destructive because tidal range is at its lowest. The highest tides are observed during new and full moons. A storm during these periods would be more destructive since storms cause tides that are higher than predicted tides.

CHAPTER 4
THE BUSINESS OF LIFE

Chapter Outline

The Ingredients of Life
    The Building Blocks
        Carbohydrates
        Proteins
        Lipids
        Nucleic Acids
    The Fuel of Life
        Photosynthesis: Making the Fuel
        Respiration: Burning the Fuel
        Primary Production
        The Importance of Nutrients
Living Machinery
    Cells and Organelles
        Primitive Cells: Prokaryotes
        Advanced Cells: Eukaryotes
    Levels of Organization
        Organization Within the Body
        Interactions Among Individuals
Challenges of Life in the Sea
    Salinity
        Diffusion and Osmosis
        Regulation of Salt and Water Balance
    Temperature
    Surface-to-Volume Ratio
Perpetuating Life
    Modes of Reproduction
        Asexual Reproduction
        Sexual Reproduction
    Reproductive Strategies
The Diversity of Life in the Sea
    Natural Selection and Adaptation
    Classifying Living Things
        The Species Concept
        Biologic Nomenclature
        Higher Taxa
        The Five Kingdoms of Life
Box: *How Did It All Begin?*

Chapter Summary

Chapter 4 presents the basic principles of biology in easy-to-read units. It is designed so that you can skip some or even all of these sections. Some of the most significant concepts are reviewed throughout the remaining chapters by means of marginal review notes so that this chapter does not have to be covered in class, especially when an introductory biology course is a prerequisite for your course.

The five fundamental units are: (1) The Ingredients of Life (basic organic molecules, photosynthesis, respiration, and primary production), (2) Living Machinery (cells and levels of organization, (3) Challenges of Live in the Sea (the principles that explain adaptations to salinity, temperature, and other demands), (4) <u>Perpetuating</u> <u>Life</u> (reproduction), and (5) <u>The</u> <u>Diversity</u> <u>of</u> <u>Life</u> <u>in</u> <u>the</u> <u>Sea</u> (evolution, phylogeny, and taxonomy).

The "tree of life" diagram shown in figure 4.24 to illustrate the five-kingdom system of classification is used as an icon in Chapters 5 to 8 to show the relative position of the groups being discussed. It is intended to help students associate the various groups into a coherent whole.

<u>Audiovisual</u> <u>Material</u>
Videos and Films:
1. <u>Photosynthesis</u> <u>and</u> <u>Respiration</u> (VHS, 30 min., color; Insight Media, 2162 Broadway, New York, NY 10024). A review of photosynthesis and respiration.
2. <u>The</u> <u>Evidence</u> <u>for</u> <u>Evolution</u> (VHS, 30 min., color; Films for the Humanities and Sciences, P.O. Box 2053, Princeton, NJ 08543; (800) 257-5126). A general presentation of the theory of evolution.
3. <u>Diversity</u> <u>of</u> <u>Life</u> (16 mm, 27 min., color; Audio-Visual Center, Indiana University, Bloomington, IN 47405; (805) 35-8087). The diversity and evolution of life on earth; characteristics and main adaptations of the five kingdoms.
4. <u>The</u> <u>Big</u> <u>Bang</u> <u>and</u> <u>Beyond</u> (VHS, 26 min., color; Films for the Humanities and Sciences, P.O. Box 2053, Princeton, NJ 08543; (800) 257-5126). A examination of how life may have originated on earth.
5. <u>Life</u> <u>Itself</u> (VHS, 23 min., color; Films for the Humanities and Sciences, P.O. Box 2053, Princeton, NJ 08543; (800) 257-5126). The characteristics of life.

Slides and Filmstrips:
1. <u>Marine</u> <u>Biogeography</u> <u>and</u> <u>Evolution</u> (20-slide set, filmstrip; Educational Images, P.O. Box 3456, Elmira, NY 14905; (800) 527-4264).
2. <u>Introducing</u> <u>Evolution</u> (6 filmstrips; Ward's, P.O. Box 92912, Rochester, NY 14692; (800) 962-2660).

<u>Software</u>
<u>Osmosis</u> <u>Lab</u> (Apple, IBM; EME, P.O. Box 2805, Danbury, CT 06813; (800) 848-2050). System where students can control variables such as ionic concentration and temperature.

<u>Answers</u> <u>to</u> <u>Thought</u> <u>Questions</u>
1. During the day, plants carry out both photosynthesis and respiration, but at night, when there is no light, they perform only respiration. Small, isolated tide pools on rocky shores are often inhabited by thick growths of seaweeds, which are plants. Would you expect the amount of oxygen to differ between night and day? How?

Oxygen dissolved in the water sharply decreases at night since the seaweeds carry out respiration but no photosynthesis. Oxygen may thus become limiting at night.

2. Some marine plants and animals are known to have high concentrations in their cells of ions found in minute amounts in seawater. Could these organisms accumulate the ions by diffusion? Formulate a hypothesis to explain how this accumulation is accomplished.

No, these marine organisms cannot accumulate these ions by diffusion. Students may be able to formulate the hypothesis (with a little help since active transport is not discussed!) that these organisms accumulate the ions by pumping them in, that is, by using energy.

CHAPTER 5
MARINE PROKARYOTES, PROTISTS, FUNGI, AND PLANTS

Chapter Summary

Chapter 5 surveys the marine organisms that are traditionally referred to as "plants." Though these organisms actually belong in four separate kingdoms, we have grouped them in a single chapter for the sake of simplicity and convenience.

Six groups of marine organisms are discussed: (1) prokaryotes (bacteria and the cyanobacteria, or blue-green algae), (2) eukaryotic, unicellular "algae" (diatoms, dinoflagellates, etc.), (3) protozoans, (4) fungi, (5) seaweeds, and (6) marine flowering plants.

The chapter covers basic information on the morphological characteristics and life histories of these organisms with a minimum of terminology. Though information about the diversity of habitats is given, specific details about the role marine plants play in the marine environment are highlighted in Chapters 9 to 15, where the ecology of various marine environments is surveyed. Salt-marsh plants and mangroves are covered in more detail in Chapter 11; kelps and seagrasses in Chapter 12. We cover not only basic general information but intriguing details to stimulate the interest of students. Their significance and economic importance is stressed throughout the chapter. There is also a section on the economic importance of seaweeds and a box on seaweeds as human food, which even includes a recipe!

Audiovisual Material
Videos and Films:

1. Algae (16 mm, 16 min., color; Audio-Visual Center, Indiana University, Bloomington, IN 47405; (812) 335-8087). The basic characteristics of the major groups of algae, including reproduction.
2. Microbial Engine: Algae and Protozoa (VHS, 36 min., color; Films for the Humanities and Sciences, P.O. Box 2053, Princeton, NJ 08543; (800) 257-5126). Diversity and ecological significance of algae and protozoans.
3. Introduction to the Protozoans (VHS, 20 min., color; Films for the Humanities and Sciences, P.O. Box 2053, Princeton, NJ 08543; (800) 257-5126). An introduction to the natural history of protozoans.
4. The Biology of Algae (VHS, 16 min., color; Insight Media, 2162 Broadway, New York, NY 10024). Biological adaptations and significance of the different groups of algae.
5. Mangrove (16 mm, 16 min., color; MTI Teleprograms, 108 Wilmont Rd., Deerfield, IL 60015). The significant ecological features of four species of mangroves.

Slides and Filmstrips:
1. Seaweeds (10- and 20-slide sets, filmstrip; Educational Images, P.O. Box 3456, Elmira, NY 14905; (800) 527-4264).
2. Marine Phytoplankton (20-slide set; Educational Images, P.O. Box 3456, Elmira, NY 14905; (800) 527-4264).
3. Diatoms (20-slide set; Educational Images, P.O. Box 3456, Elmira, NY 14905; (800) 527-4264).
4. The Tree that Walks in the Sea - The Red Mangrove (20-slide set; Educational Images, P.O. Box 3456, Elmira, NY 14905; (800) 527-4264).
5. Algae (16-slide set; Gould Media, 44 Parkway W., Mount Vernon, NY 10552; (914) 664-3285).
6. Microscopic Algae (12-slide set; Gould Media, 44 Parkway W., Mount Vernon, NY 10552; (914) 664-3285).
7. Macroscopic Algae (12-slide set; Gould Media, 44 Parkway W., Mount Vernon, NY 10552; (914) 664-3285).
8. Diatoms (20-slide set; Gould Media, 44 Parkway W., Mount Vernon, NY 10552; (914) 664-3285).
9. Algae (Diversity and Ecology) (filmstrip; Ward's, P.O. Box 92912, Rochester, NY 14692; (800) 962-2660).
10. Survey of the Algae (46-slide set; Ward's, P.O. Box 92912, Rochester, NY 14692; (800) 962-2660).
11. Diatoms (25-slide set; Ward's, P.O. Box 92912, Rochester, NY 14692; (800) 962-2660).
12. Marine Phytoplankton (20-slide set; Ward's, P.O. Box 92912, Rochester, NY 14692; (800) 962-2660).
13. Seaweeds (20-slide set; Ward's, P.O. Box 92912, Rochester, NY 14692; (800) 962-2660).
14. Biology of the Oceans - Plant Life (20-slide set; Ward's, P.O. Box 92912, Rochester, NY 14692; (800) 962-2660).

Answers to Thought Questions

1. Some biologists place the seaweeds in the kingdom Protista, others in the kingdom Plantae. Assume that a better arrangement is to group the green, brown, and red algae in their own kingdom, which we will call Macrophyta. Characterize the new kingdom by first giving its unique characteristics and then differentiate it from the protists and the true plants. Be sure to consider major exceptions or overlaps.

The hypothetical kingdom Macrophyta consists of organisms that are eukaryotic and mostly multicellular. There are some unicellular forms, however, and some consist of a multinucleated thallus. Protists, on the other hand, are also eukaryotic but unicellular. They are typically small and planktonic. Many are heterotrophs. True plants tend to show a more complex morphology, including the reproductive system. Many, such as the flowering plants, always have true leaves, stems, and roots. Like macrophytes, true plants are autotrophs. Exceptions are some specialized parasites. Students, by the way, may not be aware of some of these exceptions.

2. Only very few flowering plants have invaded the oceans, but the few marine ones are very successful. What are some possible reasons for the small number of marine flowering plants? How do those that have

taken the step manage to thrive in some environments?

One possibility is that few have evolved the necessary physiological adaptations that would allow them to overcome the osmotic demands of living in a hypersaline environment (reference should be made to the section "Challenges of Life in the Sea" in Chapter 4; problems and adaptations in salt-marsh plants are discussed in the section "Salt Marshes" in Chapter 11). Another possibility are the disadvantages inherent in fertilization that is dependent on pollination, particularly in plants that rely on insects, which are practically absent in the marine environment. Competition by already-established seaweeds is another answer that may be given by students.

CHAPTER 6
MARINE ANIMALS WITHOUT A BACKBONE

Chapter Outline

Sponges
Cnidarians: A Radially Symmetrical Body Plan
    Types of Cnidarians
        Hydrozoans
        Scyphozoans
        Anthozoans
    Biology of Cnidarians
        Digestion
        Behavior
Comb Jellies: Radial Symmetry One More Time
Bilaterally Symmetrical Worms
    Flatworms
    Ribbon Worms
    Nematodes
    Segmented Worms
        Polychaetes
        Leeches
    Odds and Ends in the World of Worms
        Peanut Worms
        Echiurans
        Beard Worms
        Arrow Worms
Lophophorates
    Bryozoans
    Phoronids
    Lamp Shells
Molluscs: The Successful Soft Body
    Types of Molluscs
        Gastropods
        Bivalves
        Cephalopods
        Other Molluscs
    Biology of Molluscs
        Digestion
        Nervous System and Behavior
        Reproduction and Life History
Arthropods: The Armored Achievers
    Crustaceans: Insects of the Sea
        The Small Crustaceans
        Shrimps, Lobsters, and Crabs
    Biology of Crustaceans
        Digestion
        Nervous System and Behavior
        Reproduction and Life History
    Other Marine Arthropods
        Horseshoe Crabs

Chapter Summary

    The chapter outlines the major groups of marine invertebrates, from sponges to protochordates. Marine protozoans are discussed in Chapter 5. Emphasis has been placed on the most important diagnostic features, general distribution, and economic importance. As in Chapters 5 to 8, terminology has been kept to a minimum. Extensive use is made of illustrations and photographs to help students understand the basic morphological and functional features of each group.

    The chapter includes short sections on the biology of the most common marine groups (cnidarians, molluscs, crustaceans, and echinoderms). Here we discuss some of the most fascinating adaptations associated with the nutrition, nervous system, behavior, reproduction, and life history of these groups. These are short and uncomplicated sections written so they can be assigned to students as supplementary material. Like the two boxes in the chapter, these sections are designed to stimulate student's curiosity.

Audiovisual Material

Videos and Films:

1. Invertebrate Zoology (Videodisc; W.C. Brown, 2460 Kerper Blvd., Dubuque, IA 52001; (800) 553-4920). Still images plus moving video of invertebrates from around the world.
2. Introduction to Invertebrates (VHS, 30 min., color; Insight Media, 2162 Broadway, New York, NY 10024). An introduction to nine of the most important animal phyla.
3. Building Bodies (VHS, 16 mm., 20 and 60 min. versions, color; Penn Communications, P.O. Box 10, Erie, PA 16512). A general introduction to the cnidarians, molluscs, echinoderms, and other marine groups. From the Life on Earth series.
4. Marine Flowers (16 mm, 30 min., color; International Film Bureau, 332 S. Michigan Ave., Chicago IL 60604; (312) 427-4545). Aspects of the biology of cnidarians and comb jellies.
5. The Portuguese Man-of-War (VHS, 9 min., color; Carolina Biological Supply, 2700 York Rd., Burlington, NC 27215; (800) 334-5551). The natural history of Physalia.
6. Octopus, Octopus (videodisc; 60 min., color; Frey Scientific, P.O. Box 8101, Mansfield, OH 44901-8101, (800) 225-3739). The natural history and behavior of octopuses in the Mediterranean and Pacific. A Jacques Cousteau film.

Slides and Filmstrips:

1. Marine Invertebrates (20-slide set, filmstrip; Educational Images, P.O. Box 3456, Elmira, NY 14905;

(800) 527-4264).

2. <u>Representative</u> <u>Marine</u> <u>Molluscs</u> (20-slide set; Educational Images, P.O. Box 3456, Elmira, NY 14905; (800) 527-4264).

3. <u>Representative</u> <u>Marine</u> <u>Arthropods</u> (20-slide set; Educational Images, P.O. Box 3456, Elmira, NY 14905; (800) 527-4264).

4. <u>Venomous</u> <u>and</u> <u>Poisonous</u> <u>Marine</u> <u>Animals</u> (20-slide set; Educational Images, P.O. Box 3456, Elmira, NY 14905; (800) 527-4264).

5. <u>The</u> <u>Invertebrates</u> (7 color film loops on marine invertebrates; Kalmia, 71 Dudley St., Cambridge, MA 02140; (617) 864-5567).

6. <u>Invertebrates</u> (several slide sets on invertebrates; Gould Media, 44 Parkway W., Mount Vernon, NY 10552; (914) 664-3285).

7. <u>The</u> <u>Lower</u> <u>Invertebrates</u> and <u>The</u> <u>Higher</u> <u>Invertebrates</u> (10 filmstrips; Educational Audiovisual, 17 Marble Ave., Pleasantville, NY 10570; (800) 431-2196).

8. <u>Marine</u> <u>Invertebrates</u> (20-slide set; JLM Visuals, 1208 Bridge St., Grafton, WI 53024-1946; (414) 377-7775, FAX (414) 377- 7750).

9. <u>The</u> <u>Invertebrates</u> (4 filmstrips; Ward's, P.O. Box 92912, Rochester, NY 14692; (800) 962-2660).

10. <u>Primitive</u> <u>Metazoan</u> <u>Phyla</u> (15-slide set; Ward's, P.O. Box 92912, Rochester, NY 14692; (800) 962-2660).

11. <u>Introduction</u> <u>to</u> <u>the</u> <u>Annelids</u> (20-slide set; Ward's, P.O. Box 92912, Rochester, NY 14692; (800) 962-2660).

12. <u>Introduction</u> <u>to</u> <u>the</u> <u>Molluscs</u> (20-slide set; Ward's, P.O. Box 92912, Rochester, NY 14692; (800) 962-2660).

13. <u>Hydroids,</u> <u>Jellyfishes,</u> <u>and</u> <u>Corals</u> (20-slide set; Ward's, P.O. Box 92912, Rochester, NY 14692; (800) 962-2660).

14. <u>Arthropods</u> <u>IV</u>: <u>Crustaceans</u> (18-slide set; Ward's, P.O. Box 92912, Rochester, NY 14692; (800) 962-2660).

15. <u>Introduction</u> <u>to</u> <u>the</u> <u>Echinoderms</u> (20-slide set; Ward's, P.O. Box 92912, Rochester, NY 14692; (800) 962-2660).

16. <u>Introduction</u> <u>to</u> <u>the</u> <u>Protochordates</u> (20-slide set; Ward's, P.O. Box 92912, Rochester, NY 14692; (800) 962-2660).

17. <u>Venomous</u> <u>and</u> <u>Poisonous</u> <u>Marine</u> <u>Animals</u> (20-slide set; Ward's, P.O. Box 92912, Rochester, NY 14692; (800) 962-2660).

Software

<u>The</u> <u>Invertebrates</u> (Mac, IBM; Frey Scientific, P.O. Box 8101, Mansfield, OH 44901-8101, (800) 225-3739). Morphology of invertebrates.

Answers to Thought Questions

1. If bilateral symmetry were to evolve among the cnidarians, in which group or groups you would expect it to occur? Why?

We would expect bilateral symmetry to develop among the mobile, non-sessile cnidarians: the jellyfishes. The adaptive advantages of bilateral symmetry (the development of a head along an anterior-posterior axis) are particularly advantageous in non-sessile animals. Parallels can be found among the echinoderms, where bilateral symmetry evolved in the group that gave rise to the sea cucumbers, most probably a non-sessile group.

2. Cephalopods, the squids, octopuses, and allies, show a much higher degree of complexity than the other groups of molluscs. What factors triggered the evolution of these changes? A rich fossil record among cephalopods shows that once they were very common and even dominant in some marine environments. Now there are only about 650 living species of cephalopods, far fewer than gastropods. In the end, were cephalopods successful? What do you think happened along the way?

15

The demands of being a predator in the pelagic realm is the fundamental reason. We can say that cephalopods were relatively successful since they did not become extinct. In fact, some unique species of squids are common in deep water (see Chapter 15). Competition by fishes, faster and more efficient swimmers, appears to be the main reason for the demise of many cephalopods. The evolution of the air-filled shell of cephalopods and its disadvantage vis-a-vis the gas bladder of fishes is briefly discussed in a box.

3. A new class of echinoderms, the sea daisies, or concentricycloids, was discovered in 1986. They are deep-water animals living on sunken wood. They are flat and round, looking very much like a small sea star without arms. They also lack a gut. Without ever having seen them, why do you think they were classified as echinoderms, not at members of a new phylum? Any hypotheses as to how they feed or move around?

Sea daisies have a water vascular system and radial symmetry, both key characteristics of echinoderms. The water vascular system consists of two concentric vascular rings (hence the class name) and tube feet. We do not know how they feed or move, so this is a good opportunity for students to think and propose some possible explanations. Sea daisies may absorb nutrients directly across a thin membrane that is located on the lower surface. This membrane can perhaps release digestive enzymes directly into the decomposing wood. The absorption of dissolved organic matter is discussed in Chapter 14. A good review of what is known about sea daisies is given on pages 725–735 by Pearse, V. et al., 1987, *Living Invertebrates*, Blackwell Scientific, Palo Alto, CA.

CHAPTER 7
MARINE FISHES

<u>Chapter Outline</u>
Vertebrates: An Introduction
Types of Fishes
    Jawless Fishes
    Cartilaginous Fishes
        Sharks
        Rays and Skates
        Ratfishes
    Bony Fishes
Biology of Fishes
    Body Shape
    Coloration
    Locomotion
    Feeding
    Digestion
    Circulatory System
    Respiratory System
        Irrigation of the Gills
        Structure of the Gills
        Gas Exchange
    Regulation of the Internal Environment
    Nervous System and Sensory Organs
    Behavior
        Territoriality
        Schooling
        Migrations
    Reproduction and Life History
        Reproductive System
        Reproductive Behavior
        Early Development
Box: *Shark!*
Box: *A Fish Called* Latimeria
<u>Chapter Summary</u>
    The chapter surveys the major groups of marine fishes and summarizes the most important aspects of their biology. The first half of the chapter introduces students to the various groups of marine fishes by outlining their most important morphological features, general distribution, and economic importance. A general classification scheme of fishes is given at the end of the chapter. Two boxes, one on shark attacks on humans and another on *Latimeria*, a living fossil, supplement this information.

    The second half deals with various aspects of the biology of marine fishes, from morphological adaptations to swimming and feeding to behavior and reproduction. It is complemented by clear and complete illustrations in case you prefer to assign one or more of these sections to students.
<u>Audiovisual Material</u>
Videos and Films:
1. The <u>Conquest</u> <u>of</u> the <u>Water</u> (VHS, 16 mm.; 20 and 60 min. versions, color; Penn Communications, P.O. Box 10, Erie, PA 16512). The general characteristic of fishes. From the <u>Life</u> <u>on</u> <u>Earth</u> series.
2. Fish (VHS, 23 min., color; Films for the Humanities and Sciences, P.O. Box 2053, Princeton, NJ

17

08543; (800) 257-5126). An introduction of the unique adaptations of fishes.

3. Inside the Shark (3/4 inch video, 16 mm; 50 min., color; WGBH TV, 125 Western Ave., Boston, MA 02134; (800) 828-9424).   The unique adaptations of sharks. From the Nova series.

4. Jaws: The True Story (VHS, 57 min., color; WGBH TV, 125 Western Ave., Boston, MA 02134; (800) 828-9424). A look at the great white shark. From the Nova series.

5. Sharks (VHS, 60 min., color; Carolina Biological Supply, 2700 York Rd., Burlington, NC 27215; (800) 334-5551). Various aspects of the biology of sharks. A Survival Anglia film.

6. The Sharks (VHS, videodisc; 60 min., color; Frey Scientific, P.O. Box 8101, Mansfield, OH 44901-8101, (800) 225-3739). Biologists study various aspects of the biology of sharks. A National Geographic Society film.

7. Lords of the Sea (VHS, 26 min., color; JLM Visuals, 1208 Bridge St., Grafton, WI 53024-1946; (414) 377-7775, FAX (414) 377-7750). Experiments conducted to analyze shark's sensory abilities.

8. Salmon on the Line (VHS, 51 min., color; Oregon Department of Fish and Game, P.O. Box 3003, Portland, OR 97208). The life cycle of the Pacific salmon; human threats to their survival.

9. Fish, Moon, and Tides: The Grunion Story (16 mm, 15 min., color; Academy Films, P.O. Box 3434, Orange, CA 92665). The life cycle and reproductive cycle of the grunion.

Slides and Filmstrips:

1. Marine Fish (15-slide set, filmstrip; Educational Images, P.O. Box 3456, Elmira, NY 14905; (800) 527-4264).

2. Fishes and Their Morphological Diversity (20-slide set; Educational Images, P.O. Box 3456, Elmira, NY 14905; (800) 527-4264).

3. Sharks (15-slide set, filmstrip; Educational Images, P.O. Box 3456, Elmira, NY 14905; (800) 527-4264).

4. The Grunion Story (25-slide set; Educational Images, P.O. Box 3456, Elmira, NY 14905; (800) 527-4264).

5. Introduction to the Bony Fishes (20-slide set; Educational Images, P.O. Box 3456, Elmira, NY 14905; (800) 527-4264).

6. Introduction to the Cartilaginous Fishes (20-slide set; Educational Images, P.O. Box 3456, Elmira, NY 14905; (800) 527-4264).

7. Sharks of the World (20-slide set; Educational Images, P.O. Box 3456, Elmira, NY 14905; (800) 527-4264).

Software

Sharks: Their Nature and Evolution (Apple; Educational Images, P.O. Box 3456, Elmira, NY 14905; (800) 527-4264). Introduction to the biology of sharks.

Answers to Thought Questions

1. Hagfishes and lampreys are the only living representatives of a very ancient group. Why do you suppose there are still some of these jawless fishes around?

Some still survive but as highly specialized forms (as parasites and unusual predators) that have not been outcompeted by the more advanced fishes.

2. A deep-water shark, new to science, is collected for the first time. The specimen is studied in detail, but its stomach is empty. How could you get a rough idea of its feeding habits? The specimen is a female, and its reproductive tract is found to contain 20 eggs. Can you tell the type of development characteristic of this species?

We can get an idea of its feeding habits by looking at the type of teeth it has (see if it is a carnivore with well-developed teeth or if it has reduced or absent teeth as in filter feeders), perhaps by the relative size and/or shape of its mouth, and the presence or absence of filtering gill rakers. We can tell about the type of development by the relative size and number of eggs: ovoviviparous and viviparous sharks tend to have few eggs. An egg case would indicate that eggs are eventually released and that the species is oviparous.

3. Individuals of some species of bony fishes change sex, some to maintain more males than females, others more females than males. What are the advantages and disadvantages of each situation? Are there any advantages and disadvantages in having an equal number of males and females?

It is not always easy to explain the biological significance of sex ratios as observed in nature, hence the value of this question as a discussion topic! Having more females that males can be seen as advantageous since fewer males are needed to fertilize females: one male can fertilize several females. It is more expensive, however, to be a female since eggs contain stored nutrients and in many fishes large numbers of eggs are produced to ensure the survival of the species. If the number of females is higher than that of males, the species as a whole must utilize more food resources. Having more males than females can be advantageous for the survival of the species in cases where males are more aggressive than females. The relative "value" of each sex, however, depends on their behavior. Females can be more aggressive or males can be particularly "valuable" if involved in nest-making or in the defense of territories. It can be argued, however, that the best strategy is to maintain an equal number of males and females to prevent a slow down in the reproductive rate of the species in case of increased mortality in one of the two sexes as a result of disease, increased predation, or other factors.

CHAPTER 8
MARINE REPTILES, BIRDS, AND MAMMALS

Chapter Outline

Marine Reptiles
    Sea Turtles
    Sea Snakes
    Other Marine Reptiles
Seabirds
    Penguins
    Tubenoses
    Pelicans and Allies
    Gulls and Allies
    Shorebirds
Marine Mammals
    Types of Marine Mammals
        Seals, Sea Lions, and Walruses
        Sea Otters
        Manatees and Dugongs
        Whales, Dolphins, and Porpoises
    Biology of Marine Mammals
        Swimming and Diving
        Echolocation
        Behavior
        Migrations
        Reproduction
Box: *The Whales that Walked to Sea*
Box: *The Other "Big Bang" Theory*
Box: *How Intelligent Are Cetaceans?*

Chapter Summary

Chapter 8 discusses the marine tetrapods. Marine reptiles and birds are covered by providing information about their morphological characteristics, general distribution, and the most outstanding features of their biology, particularly feeding and behavior. Some detailed information on the current status of sea turtles is also given.

The chapter emphasizes the marine mammals, particularly the cetaceans, a group among the favorite of students. The various groups of marine mammals are introduced by discussing general morphology, distribution, and feeding. An up-to-date and more detailed section on the biology of marine mammals discusses swimming and diving (including a novel "flip the pages" scheme to explain swimming in cetaceans), echolocation, behavior, migrations, and reproduction. It is supplemented by a new box on recent discoveries on the evolution of whales, another on a new hypothesis that helps explain the origin and function of echolocation in whales, and a third box on intelligence in dolphins. Whaling is discussed in the section "The Case of the Whales" in Chapter 17.

Audiovisual Material

Videos and Films:

1. <u>The Marine Iguana: Variations on a Theme</u> (16 mm, 23 min., color; University of California Extension Media Center; 2176 Shattuck Ave., Berkeley, CA 94704; (415) 642-0460). A look at the marine iguana of the Galápagos Islands.
2. <u>Sea Turtles: Ancient Nomads</u> (VHS, 60 min., color; Carolina Biological Supply, 2700 York Rd., Burlington, NC 27215; (800) 334-5551). The natural history and behavior of sea turtles. An Audubon

film.

3. Colonial Birds: The Gull's Way and the Penguin's Way (VHS, 40 min., color, filmstrip; Educational Images, P.O. Box 3456, Elmira, NY 14905; (800) 527-4264). Social behavior and natural history of the ring-billed gull and the Adélie penguin.

4. Audubon Society's Video Guide to the Birds of North America (Volume 2 - seabirds) (VHS, 60 min., color; Media Design Associates, P.O. Box 3189, Boulder, CA 80307). A survey of shorebirds and other seabirds.

5. King Penguin (VHS, 60 min., color; Carolina Biological Supply, 2700 York Rd., Burlington, NC 27215; (800) 334-5551). Natural history of the king penguin. A Survival Anglia film.

6. The Flight of the Penguins (VHS, 60 min., color; Carolina Biological Supply, 2700 York Rd., Burlington, NC 27215; (800) 334-5551). The natural history of penguins in Antarctica. A Jacques Cousteau film.

7. Wild Seas/Wild Seals (VHS, 60 min., color; Carolina Biological Supply, 2700 York Rd., Burlington, NC 27215; (800) 334-5551). The natural history and reproductive behavior of the gray seal. A Survival Anglia film.

8. The Forgotten Mermaids (VHS, 60 min., color; Carolina Biological Supply, 2700 York Rd., Burlington, NC 27215; (800) 334-5551). The manatee in Florida. A Jacques Cousteau film.

9. The Unsinkable Sea Otter (videodisc; 60 min., color; Frey Scientific, P.O. Box 8101, Mansfield, OH 44901-8101, (800) 225-3739). The sea otter in Alaska and California. A Jacques Cousteau film.

10. Smile of the Walrus (videodisc; 60 min., color; Carolina Biological Supply, 2700 York Rd., Burlington, NC 27215; (800) 334-5551). The walrus in Alaska. A Jacques Cousteau film.

11. Whales, Dolphins and Men (16 mm, 52 min., color; BBC TV, 630 Fifth Ave., New York, NY 10020). A portrait of cetaceans, including an outdated look at whaling. From the Nova series.

12. Whale Watch (VHS, videodisc; 60 min., color; Frey Scientific, P.O. Box 8101, Mansfield, OH 44901-8101, (800) 225-3739). The comeback of the gray whale. From the Nova series.

13. Whale Rescue (VHS, 16 mm; 52 min., color; Coronet/MTI Film and Video, 108 Wilmont Rd., Deerfield, IL 60015; (800) 323-5343). The rescue of beached pilot whales on Cape Cod. From the Nova series.

14. The Great Whales (VHS, videodisc; 60 min., color; Frey Scientific, P.O. Box 8101, Mansfield, OH 44901-8101, (800) 225-3739). An introduction to the distribution and biology of whales. A National Geographic Society film.

15. Sign of the Apes, Songs of the Whales (VHS, videodisc; 60 min., color; Frey Scientific, P.O. Box 8101, Mansfield, OH 44901-8101, (800) 225-3739). An exploration of the ability of whales to communicate among themselves and with humans. From the Nova series.

16. Whales! (VHS, 60 min., color; Carolina Biological Supply, 2700 York Rd., Burlington, NC 27215; (800) 334-551). A general introduction to the whales. An Audubon film.

17. The Blue Whale (VHS, 28 min., color; Films for the Humanities and Sciences, P.O. Box 2053, Princeton, NJ 08543; (800) 257-5126). The blue whale in the Gulf of California.

18. Magnificent Monsters of the Deep (VHS, 60 min., color; Carolina Biological Supply, 2700 York Rd., Burlington, NC 27215; (800) 334-5551). The southern right whale in Patagonia. A Survival Anglia film.

19. Gentle Giants of the Pacific (VHS, 60 min., color; Carolina Biological Supply, 2700 York Rd., Burlington, NC 27215; (800) 334-5551). The humpback whale in Hawaii. A Survival Anglia film.

20. The Desert Whales (VHS, 60 min., color; Carolina Biological Supply, 2700 York Rd., Burlington, NC 27215; (800) 334-5551). The annual migration of the gray whale. A Jacques Cousteau film.

21. The Singing Whale (VHS, 60 min., color; Carolina Biological Supply, 2700 York Rd., Burlington, NC 27215; (800) 334-5551). The songs of the humpback whale in the Caribbean. A Jacques Cousteau film.

22. Killer Whales (VHS, 40 min., color; Educational Images, P.O. Box 3456, Elmira, NY 14905; (800)

527-4264). Natural history and behavior of killer whales.
23. Whales and Whaling (16 mm, 25 min., color; Media Guild, 11722 Sorrento Valley Rd., San Diego, CA 92121; (619) 755-9191). An outdated but informative look at the history of whaling and its impact on the survival of whales.
24. The Private Lives of Dolphins (VHS, 60 min., color; Films for the Humanities and Sciences, P.O. Box 2053, Princeton, NJ 08543; (800) 257-5126). Reviews recent studies on the social system of dolphins.

Record and Cassette:

Ocean of Song: Whale Voices (12 in stereo record, cassette; Carolina Biological Supply, 2700 York Rd., Burlington, NC 27215; (800) 334-5551). Recordings of humpback and killer whales.

Slides and Filmstrips:

1. Marine Reptiles (10-slide set, filmstrip; Educational Images, P.O. Box 3456, Elmira, NY 14905; (800) 527-4264).
2. Sea Birds (15-slide set, filmstrip; Educational Images, P.O. Box 3456, Elmira, NY 14905; (800) 527-4264).
3. Wading Birds (20-slide set; Educational Images, P.O. Box 3456, Elmira, NY 14905; (800) 527-4264).
4. Adaptation and Biology of Seabirds (40-slide set; Educational Images, P.O. Box 3456, Elmira, NY 14905; (800) 527-4264).
5. Birds of the High Seas (20-slide set; JLM Visuals, 1208 Bridge St., Grafton, WI 53024-1946; (414) 377-7775, FAX (414) 377-7750).
6. Marine Mammals (19-slide set, filmstrip; Educational Images, P.O. Box 3456, Elmira, NY 14905; (800) 527-4264).
7. Whales and Dolphins (20-slide set; Educational Images, P.O. Box 3456, Elmira, NY 14905; (800) 527-4264).
8. Biology of Whales (21-slide set, filmstrip; Educational Images, P.O. Box 3456, Elmira, NY 14905; (800) 527-4264).
9. Whales and Dolphins (20-slide set; Ward's, P.O. Box 92912, Rochester, NY 14692; (800) 962-2660).
10. Killer Whales (filmstrip; Educational Images, P.O. Box 3456, Elmira, NY 14905; (800) 527-4264).
11. Killer Whales - Lords of the Sea (2 filmstrips; Ward's, P.O. Box 92912, Rochester, NY 92912; (800) 962-2660).
12. Marine Mammals (25-slide set; JLM Visuals, 1208 Bridge St., Grafton, WI 53024-1946; (414) 377-7775, FAX (414) 377-7750).

Software

Whales of the World: Great and Small (Apple; Educational Images, P.O. Box 3456, Elmira, NY 14905; (800) 527-4264). Description and status of whales and dolphins.

Answers to Thought Questions

1. Sea turtles have disappeared from many regions, and one way of trying to save them is to reintroduce them to areas where they have been wiped out. This is done by reburying eggs or by releasing newborn baby turtles on beaches. Why are eggs reburied or baby turtles released instead of fully grown individuals?

The newly-born sea turtles appear to become imprinted to the beach where they are born. Eggs must then be reburied or baby turtles released at specific beaches if we want adults to return to these beaches to nest. Such techniques are being used in efforts to introduce the rare Kemp's ridley sea turtle in Texas, which nests on only one beach in Mexico.

2. Most seabirds are specialists that feed on particular types of fish and other prey. In some cases this may reduce the chances of competing with other species of seabirds for limited resources. Sometimes, however, we find two or more species of seabirds feeding on the same type of fish. What type of mechanisms might have evolved to prevent direct competition?

Seabirds that feed on the same type of food may prevent competing with each other by nesting on different areas (open spaces versus holes in cliffs, for instance) or nesting at different times of the year.
3. Cetaceans give birth to few well-developed calves at well-spaced intervals. They also feed and protect the calves for long periods. This is in sharp contrast to most fishes, in which many eggs are spawned and the parents spend no time feeding and protecting the offspring. What do you think is the best strategy? Has this effort paid off in the case of the great whales?

There is no "correct" answer to this question! It is intended to make students think. Each species has evolved a particular reproductive strategy depending on a number of factors: size, longevity, predator pressure to name a few. Unfortunately, the particular strategy of cetaceans has definitely worked against their chances of survival. Whaling and its effect on the population size of the great whales is discussed in the section "The Case of the Whales" in Chapter 17.

CHAPTER 9
AN INTRODUCTION TO ECOLOGY

Chapter Outline

The Organization of Communities
    How Populations Grow
    Ways That Species Interact
        Competition
        Eating Each Other
        Living Together
The Flow of Energy and Materials
    Trophic Structure
        Trophic Levels
        The Trophic Pyramid
        Measuring Primary Productivity
        Standing Stock
    Cycles of Essential Nutrients
Biological Zonation of the Marine Environment
Box: *Symbiosis and the Modern Cell*
Box: *Biodiversity: All Creatures Great and Small*

Chapter Summary

The basic principles of ecology are discussed in Chapter 9. It introduces students to Part III of the book where the different types of marine environments are discussed (Chapters 10 to 15). It is brief chapter that covers some elementary principles of population dynamics, species interactions (competition, predation, and symbioses), energy flow (including a section on the measurement of primary productivity), and nutrient cycles. Many of these fundamental concepts are integrated and reviewed in the upcoming chapters by means of marginal review notes. The food web diagram in figure 9.12 uses arrows that are color coded to allow comparison with other food webs throughout the book. Chapter 9 may then be omitted, particularly in cases where students have a basic biology course as a prerequisite. An alternative is to assign specific sections (the section on the measurement of primary productivity is a good suggestion) as needed when Chapters 10 to 15 are covered.

Chapter 9 concludes with a scheme of the classification of the marine environment. We have used the most widely accepted scheme, one which unfortunately is not universally used. The zonation scheme introduced in figure 9.20 is used as an icon in Chapters 10 to 15. This feature not only reinforces the concept of zonation but tells students which environment is being covered at a glance and ties together all six chapters that survey the marine environment.

For the concept of detritus, which is first introduced in this chapter, we have used the widely accepted but not universal definition of non-living organic matter together with bacteria. This is an operational useful definition that takes into account the fact that in its ecological context bacteria are nearly impossible to separate from the organic matter.

Audiovisual Material

Videos and Films:

1. Marine Ecology (16 mm, 27 min., color; CRM Films, 2233 Faraday Ave., Carlsbad, CA 92008; (619) 431-9800). A simple film that illustrates some of the basic principles of marine ecology, including limiting factors and productivity.
2. Principles of Ecology (VHS, 23 min., color; Films for the Humanities and Sciences, P.O. Box 2053, Princeton, NJ 08543; (800) 257-5126). The planet as a giant living organism.
3. Antarctica: Earth's Last Frontier (3/4 inch video; 57 min., color; WGBH TV, 125 Western Ave.,

Boston, MA 02134; (800) 828-9424). From the Nova series. It discusses marine food webs in Antarctica.
4. Strange Partners, Symbiosis and the Sea (16 mm, 12 min., color; Films, Inc., 5547 Ravenswood Ave., Chicago, IL 60640). Examples of symbiotic associations in the marine environment.

Slides and Filmstrips:
1. Marine Food Webs (20-slide set, filmstrip; Educational Images, P.O. Box 3456, Elmira, NY 14905; (800) 527-4264).
2. Marine Productivity (15-slide set, filmstrip; Educational Images, P.O. Box 3456, Elmira, NY 14905; (800) 527-4264).
3. Light and Primary Productivity (20-slide set, filmstrip; Educational Images, P.O. Box 3456, Elmira, NY 14905; (800) 527-4264).
4. Nutrient Cycles (20-slide set, filmstrip; Educational Images, P.O. Box 3456, Elmira, NY 14905; (800) 527-4264).
5. Algal Symbiosis (10-slide set, filmstrip; Educational Images, P.O. Box 3456, Elmira, NY 14905; (800) 527-4264).
6. Introduction to Ecology (sound filmstrip; Ward's, P.O. Box 92912, Rochester, NY 14692; (800) 962-2660).
7. Survey of Marine Communities (40-slide set; JLM Visuals, 1208 Bridge St., Grafton, WI 53024-1946; (414) 377-7775, FAX (414) 377-7750).

Answers to Thought Questions

1. Two species of sea urchins live practically side by side in sandy bottoms. The two species appear to have the same diet: drift seaweeds and other bits of organic matter. They are able to live in the same environment without competing with each other. How might they be able to share their habitat and food resources?

Competition may be prevented by being active and feeding at different times of the day, by feeding at different levels in the sand (we say they "appear to have the same diet" but there may be slight differences due to the possibility that one species picks up organic material slightly deeper in the sand that the other, perhaps because the teeth of the Aristotle's lantern are longer), by feeding in different areas (we say they live "side by side" but one of them may migrate to nearby rocky bottoms at night to graze on a different type of food), and differential ability to digest the drift algae and/or organic matter (one of the two species may be unable to actually digest part of the ingested food). Students may not know these details but this is a good place to introduce them to some concepts and ideas. Some aspects of the ecology of subtidal sea urchins are presented in the section "Kelp Communities" in Chapter 12; the use of dissolved organic matter (DOM) by marine invertebrates is discussed in the section "The Microbial Loop" in Chapter 14.

2. It is not always easy to categorize a particular case of symbiosis. Suppose a certain species of snail is always found living on a certain coral. No one has found evidence that the snail harms the coral, so the relationship is classified as an example of commensalism. How would you go about testing this hypothesis? What kinds of observations might lead to the conclusion that the snail is a parasite, or that it has a mutualistic relationship with the coral?

"Harm" is not always easy to detect. In this hypothetical case (though snails are found in association with different types of corals) drastic reactions in infected coral colonies such as injured or dead tissue or even bleaching, the release of zooxanthellae, may not take place. Less subtle responses in infected coral can be hypothesized: abnormal feeding behavior in polyps, a decrease in the growth rate, or a decrease in the release of planula larvae. This symbiosis may prove to be mutualistic if for example the coral obtains nutrients from mucus produced by the snail or the snail somehow protects the coral against predators. This question assumes some previous knowledge of corals, which are introduced in the section "Types of Cnidarians" in Chapter 6; additional details on the biology of corals are given in Chapter 13. The instructor may also bring in examples (actual cases or hypothetical) that involve other marine invertebrates that may be more familiar to students: polychaete worms or various types of crustaceans living on echinoderms, flat worms or crustaceans in bivalves, etc.

CHAPTER 10
BETWEEN THE TIDES

Chapter Summary

Chapter 10 surveys intertidal communities. They are by far the best known and most accessible of all marine communities, hence the need for a relatively lengthy chapter.

Rocky shore communities are examined by first outlining how the demands of physical factors (type of substrate, exposure to air by tides, and wave action) are met by intertidal organisms. Morphological as well as behavioral adaptations are highlighted. We found this the most appropriate place to briefly discuss refraction and the distribution of wave energy along the coast.

The chapter emphasizes how biological factors influence community structure. It incorporates results of some of the most current approaches in the study of rocky shore communities. We specifically discuss competition for space, grazing, predation, availability of food, feeding interrelationships, how these and other factors influence vertical zonation, and ecological succession. The food web diagram in figure 10.32 uses arrows that are color coded to allow comparison with other food webs in Chapter 9 and elsewhere in the book.

The chapter concludes with an examination of the unique characteristics of soft-bottom intertidal communities, those established on muddy and sandy bottoms. The types of sediments and their distribution are first examined, followed by a look at how organisms are adapted to the availability of oxygen, and motility, feeding, and zonation patterns in soft bottoms.

A box on transplantation, removal, and caging experiments gives students a good idea of what marine biologists actually do! It also reinforces material on the scientific method and experimentation that was introduced in Chapter 1.

It should be emphasized that, as in the rest of the book, we use examples of both the Atlantic and Pacific coasts of North America in addition to some from other parts of the world. We realize, however, that every intertidal area is different and as a result we have tried to distill some simple general patterns from several well-established sources. So please excuse us if we were forced to omit an important organism that occurs in your area!

Reference should be made to the map on Appendix D that outlines the major coastal communities of North America. A list of field guides that can be used from Hawaii to the Caribbean supplements the map. Our list emphasizes general, easy-to-use field guides rather than the more specialized references on the classification of different marine groups.

Audiovisual Material

Videos and Films:

1. Marine Animals of the Open Coast: A Study of Adaptation (16 mm, 22 min., color; Martin Moyer Productions, 900 Federal Ave., Seattle WA 98102). The major adaptations among animals inhabiting rocky and sandy shores.
2. The Margins of the Land (VHS, 16 mm; 55 min., color; Ambrose Video Publishing, 1290 Avenue of the Americas, New York, NY 10104; (800) 526-4663). A survey of the major intertidal communities. From The Living Planet series.
3. Life on Seashores (VHS, 16 mm; 24 min., color; Media Guild, 11722 Sorrento Valley Rd., San Diego, CA 92121; (619) 755-9191). A contrast between life on rocky and sandy shores. A BBC TV film.
4. Zonation on a Marine Rock Platform (16 mm, 17 min., color; Films, Inc., 5547 Ravenswood Ave., Chicago, IL 60640). Zonation patterns, indicator species, and their adaptations.
5. Coastlines (VHS, 28 mn., color; Films for the Humanities and Sciences, P.O. Box 2053, Princeton, NJ 08543; (800) 257-5126). A survey of life along different types of coastlines. From the Man and the Biosphere series.

Slides and Filmstrips:

1. Beaches (15-slide set, filmstrip; Educational Images, P.O. Box 3456, Elmira, NY 14905; (800) 527-4264).
2. The Rocky Shore Biome (20-slide set; Educational Images, P.O. Box 3456, Elmira, NY 14905; (800) 527-4264).
3. Intertidal Communities (40-slide set, filmstrip; Educational Images, P.O. Box 3456, Elmira, NY 14905; (800) 527-4264).
4. Principles of Seashore Ecology (40-slide set; Educational Images, P.O. Box 3456, Elmira, NY 14905; (800) 527-4264).
5. Zonation of Seaweeds and Animals (50-slide set; Educational Images, P.O. Box 3456, Elmira, NY 14905; (800) 527-4264).
6. Life on Piers and Pilings (20-slide set; Educational Images, P.O. Box 3456, Elmira, NY 14905; (800) 527-4264).
7. Ecology of a Sandy Beach (20-slide set; Educational Images, P.O. Box 3456, Elmira, NY 14905; (800) 527-4264).
8. The Seashore and its Seaweed Ecology (24-slide set; Gould Media, 44 Park W., Mount Vernon, New York, NY 10552; (914) 664-3285).
9. The Ecology of Seashore Animals (24-slide set; Gould Media, 44 Park W., Mount Vernon, New York, NY 10552; (914) 664-3285).
10. Principles of Seashore Ecology (40-slide set; Gould Media, 44 Park W., Mount Vernon, New York, NY 10552; (914) 664-3285).
11. The Ecology of Rocky Coasts (filmstrip; Ward's, P.O. Box 92912, Rochester, NY 14692; (800) 962-2660).
12. The Ecology of Sandy Beaches (filmstrip; Ward's, P.O. Box 92912, Rochester, NY 14692; (800) 962-2660).
13. Seashore Inhabitants (20-slide set; Ward's, P.O. Box 92912, Rochester, NY 14692; (800) 962-2660).

14. <u>Tide</u> <u>Pool</u> <u>Life</u> <u>of</u> <u>the</u> <u>Atlantic</u> (20-slide set; JLM Visuals, 1208 Bridge St., Grafton, WI 53024-1946; (414) 377-7775, FAX (414) 377-7750).
15. <u>Intertidal</u> <u>Organisms</u> <u>of</u> <u>the</u> <u>West</u> <u>Coast</u> <u>Rocky</u> <u>Shore</u> (20-slide set; JLM Visuals, 1208 Bridge St., Grafton, WI 53024-1946; (414) 377-7775, FAX (414) 377-7750).
16. <u>Life</u> <u>of</u> <u>Rocky</u> <u>Caribbean</u> <u>Seashores</u> (25-slide set; JLM Visuals, 1208 Bridge St., Grafton, WI 53024-1946; (414) 377-7775), FAX (414) 377-7750).

Software

<u>Shore</u> <u>Features</u> (Apple; Educational Images, P.O. Box 3456, Elmira, NY 14905; (800) 527-4264). Identification of the basic characteristics of shores.

Answers to Thought Questions

1. There are marked differences in the type of organisms found at four different locations at the same tidal height along a rocky shore. What might account for this? Offer at least three possible explanations.

Differences in the type of organisms may be due to differences in physical factors such as exposure to wave action, the type of rocky substrate (stability and other particulars of the surface including color: at low tide darker substrates may absorb more heat than light substrates), relative exposure to light, abrasion by sand due to proximity to a sandy shore, and the presence of seeping fresh water and/or pollutants. In addition differences may be the direct result of biotic factors (food, predation, and/or competition for space) that may be influenced or determined by one or more of the physical factors mentioned above.

2. Most marine biologists hypothesize that space, not food, limits populations in the rocky intertidal. What kind of experiments could be performed to test this hypothesis?

One type of experiment may involve the removal of individuals of a dominant species that lives in dense patches (such as mussels, seaweeds, or barnacles) and see what type of organisms will settle or move in. Individuals are removed in such a way as to leave patches of varying densities (or different areas covered in the case of seaweeds). All other factors, including food (and light in the case of seaweeds) remain unchanged; untouched patches are left as controls. Space would be shown to be limiting if the number of species in the manipulated patches is higher than in the control patches.

CHAPTER 11
ESTUARIES: WHERE RIVERS MEET THE SEA

Chapter Outline

Origins and Types of Estuaries
Physical Characteristics of Estuaries
    Salinity
    Substrate
    Other Physical Factors
Estuaries as Ecosystems
    Living in an Estuary
        Coping with Salinity
        Adapting to the Mud
    Types of Estuarine Communities
        Open Water
        Mud Flats
        Salt Marshes
        Mangrove Forests
        Other Estuarine Communities
    Feeding Interactions Among Estuarine Organisms
Box: *Life in the Mud*
Box: *Fiddler on the Mud*

Chapter Summary

Though they are intertidal, coastal communities along estuaries are important enough to merit their inclusion in a separate chapter.

The chapter opens with a discussion of the origins and classification of estuaries. The student is then introduced to the unique physical and chemical characteristic of estuaries: wide fluctuations in salinity and temperature, muddy substrates, low oxygen content of sediments, and high water turbidity. Emphasis is placed on how estuarine organisms are adapted to these particular demands. the most significant adaptations associated with the maintenance of salt balance are considered in some detail.

The rest of the chapter examines the distribution of life in the most distinctive estuarine communities. We have categorized them into those characteristic of four major habitats: open water, mud flats, salt marshes, and mangrove forests. Mangroves, though not strictly estuarine in distribution, are discussed here since they are typically found along the margin of tropical estuaries. Also mentioned are seagrass communities, which are covered in more detail in Chapter 12, and oyster reefs. Food webs and primary productivity of estuarine communities in general are discussed in the concluding section of the chapter, one that intends to highlight the significance of estuaries in the economy of coastal ecosystems.

Information on estuarine communities is supplemented by two boxes. A box on meiofauna deal with the fascinating life found in a very particular environment; a second box examines some of the unique behavioral adaptations of fiddler crabs to life in mud flats.

Audiovisual Material

Videos and Films:

1. The Sea Behind the Dunes (VHS, 16 mm; 58 min., color; WGBH TV, 125 Western Ave., Boston, MA 02134; (800) 828-9424). A year-long look at life in a salt marsh near Cape Cod. From the Nova series.

2. The Back Bay (16 mm, 20 min., color; United States Department of the Interior, C and 19st St., NW, Washington, DC 20242). The mud-flat and salt-marsh communities in a southern California estuary.

3. Ecology of a Tidal Slough (16 mm, 20 min., color; United States Department of the Interior, C and 19st St., NW, Washington, DC 20242). The mud-flat and salt-marsh communities in a northern California estuary.
4. The Salt Marshes: Border Between Sea and Land (16 mm, 23 min., color; MTI Teleprograms, 108 Wilmont Rd, Deerfield, IL 60015). A portrait of north Atlantic salt marshes.
5. The Salt Marsh: A Question of Values (16 mm, 22 min., color; Encyclopedia Britannica, 310 S. Michigan Ave., Chicago, IL 60604; (312) 321-7105). Documents measurement of primary productivity in salt marshes on the east coast of the U.S.; effects of human intrusion.
6. Secrets of the Salt Marsh (VHS, 20 min., color; Insight Media, 2162 Broadway, New York, NY 10024). An overview of the ecology of salt marshes
7. The Margins of the Land (VHS, 16 mm; 55 min., color; Ambrose Video Publishing, 1290 Avenue of the Americas, New York, NY 10104; (800) 526-4663). The film, from the Living Planet series, discusses mangrove forests as well as other types of coastal communities.
8. Salt Marshes—A Special Resource (VHS, 28 min., color; Educational Images, P.O. Box 3456, Elmira, NY 14905; (800) 527-4264).
9. Mangrove (16 mm, 16 min., color; MTI Teleprograms, 108 Wilmont Rd., Deerfield, IL 60015). The significant ecological features of four species of mangroves.
10. Creatures of the Mangrove (VHS, 60 min., color; Carolina Biological Supply, 2700 York Rd., Burlington, NC 27215; (800) 334-5551). The fascinating inhabitants of mangrove forests in Borneo. A National Geographic Society film.

Slides and Filmstrips:
1. Estuaries (20-slide set, filmstrip; Carolina Biological Supply, 2700 York Rd., Burlington, NC 27215; (800) 334-5551).
2. The Salt Marsh Biome (20-slide set; Carolina Biological Supply, 2700 York Rd., Burlington, NC 27215; (800) 334-5551).
3. The Ecology of Estuaries (20-slide set; Gould Media, 44 Parkway W., Mount Vernon, NY 10552; (914) 664-3285).
4. The Ecology of Saltmarshes (24-slide set; Carolina Biological Supply, 2700 York Rd., Burlington, NC 27215; (800) 334-5551).
5. Ecology of the Salt Water Marsh (20-slide set; JLM Visuals, 1208 Bridge St., Grafton, WI 53024-1946; (414) 377-7775, FAX (414) 377-7750).
6. Evolution of the Salt Water Marsh (20-slide set; JLM Visuals, 1208 Bridge St., Grafton, WI 53024-1946; (414) 377-7775, FAX (414) 377-7750).
7. Ecology of Mud Flats (filmstrip; Ward's, P.O. Box 92912, Rochester, NY 14692; (800) 962-2660).
8. Salt Marshes - A Special Resource (filmstrip; Ward's, P.O. Box 92912, Rochester, NY 14692; (800) 962-2660).
9. The Salt Marsh Biome (20-slide set; Ward's, P.O. Box 92912, Rochester, NY 14692; (800) 962-2660).

Answers to Thought Questions
1. A proposal is made to deepen the entrance and main channel of an estuary. What do you think will happen to the salt marshes that surround the channel? What do you predict will happen to the primary production of the estuary as a whole?
The deepening of the entrance and main channel of an estuary would adversely affect or simply destroy salt marshes in the vicinity. Wave action will increase and the effect of the tides that normally flow into the salt marshes is minimized. Primary production of the estuary is expected to drop significantly.
2. Some of the organic material manufactured in estuarine communities is exported to other ecosystems. What type of ecosystems receive this material? How is this material transported?

The organic material that is exported is mostly in the form of fine detritus. It will be carried out of the estuary with the low tide and transported by currents to neighboring rocky and sandy shores, as well as to subtidal and deep-water communities.

CHAPTER 12
LIFE ON THE CONTINENTAL SHELF

Chapter Outline

Physical Characteristics of the Subtidal Environment
The Continental Shelf as an Ecosystem
    Soft-Bottom Subtidal Communities
        Unvegetated Soft-Bottom Communities
        Seagrass Beds
    Hard-Bottom Subtidal Communities
        Rocky Bottoms
        Kelp Communities

Box: *Antarctica: The Last Frontier*
Box: *Cleaning Symbiosis*

Chapter Summary

The subtidal environment, particularly its benthos, is the subject of Chapter 12. Coral reefs, though subtidal, are covered in Chapter 13.

The first section of the chapter defines the subtidal environment and outlines the most significant physical factors that influence subtidal communities. The rest of the chapter is devoted to the major subtidal communities, which are classified into soft-bottom and hard-bottom communities.

The section on soft-bottom communities, the most widely distributed of all subtidal communities, includes material on patterns of distribution and habitat selection, including a timely discussion of the lottery hypothesis. Deposit and suspension feeding, already mentioned in previous chapters, are discussed here in more detail, particularly in reference to the factors that influence their distribution in soft sediments. Seagrass beds, which were introduced in Chapter 5, are covered here as an example of a community typical of soft bottoms around the world. We emphasize their ecological significance as a highly productive ecosystem and as a habitat for other species.

The chapter concludes with a discussion of hard-bottom subtidal communities. The general characteristics of these communities are discussed first. Attention is placed on the effects of competition for space, grazing, and predation. Kelp beds and forests, among the most productive and fascinating of all marine communities, are discussed as examples of hard-bottom communities. We examine up-to-date information on their geographic and local distribution, life history, vertical and horizontal zonation, and the role of grazing and physical factors on their maintenance.

Chapter 12 includes a box on the unique subtidal communities of Antarctica and another on cleaning symbiosis, an example of a complex biological interaction in the marine environment.

Audiovisual Material

Film:

The Poisoned Sea (16 mm, 27 min., color; Moonlight Productions, 2243 Old Middlefield Way, Mountain View, CA 94043). The effects of pollution and grazing on southern California kelp forests.

Slides and Filmstrips:

1. Subtidal Communities (15-slide set, filmstrip; Educational Images, P.O. Box 3456, Elmira, NY 14905; (800) 527-4264).
2. Benthic Communities (15-slide set, filmstrip; Educational Images, P.O. Box 3456, Elmira, NY 14905; (800) 527-4264).
3. Subtidal Marine Invertebrates of North America (40-slideset; Educational Images, P.O. Box 3456, Elmira, NY 14905; (800) 527-4264).
4. The Kelp Forest (20-slide set; Educational Images, P.O. Box 3456, Elmira, NY 14905; (800) 527-4264).

1. Eelgrass communities in Europe and the eastern coast of North America were severely affected by a still unknown disease. The so-called eelgrass blight or wasting disease of the 1930s caused many eelgrass beds to disappear. What changes would you expect to take place if an eelgrass community vanishes from a given area? Consider changes to the substrate, the benthos, and other types of marine animals. Are there any possible changes among animals living on land? What type of community do you think replaced the eelgrass communities after they disappeared?

The disappearance of an eelgrass community causes an increase in water turbulence, which increases the amount of suspended particles in the water. There is a decrease in the clarity of the water and a reduction in light penetration through the water column as a result. Eelgrass stabilizes the sediment so that, together with an increase in turbulence, finer particles, which include detritus, will be carried away and larger particles will be deposited on the bottom sediment. This, together with the decrease in detritus, will induce a decrease in the number of deposit feeders and an increase in suspension feeders. A highly productive eelgrass community will be replaced by a soft-bottom community dominated by suspension feeders and few or no primary producers. The total number of species will be lower since the organisms that live associated with eelgrass will also disappear. Animals that use the eelgrass community as a nursery will decrease in number. The export of detritus to other communities will sharply decrease. The disappearance of an eelgrass community may also affect land animals. Drifting leaves, many of which normally accumulate along the shore, serve as an important food source to land animals such as insects.

2. The life history of kelps consists of a very large sporophyte and a tiny gametophyte. Sea lettuce and some other seaweeds, however, have a gametophyte that is as big as their sporophyte (see figure 5.21 *a*). Do you see any advantages for kelps having such an inconspicuous, puny gametophyte?

One possible advantage of having a small gametophyte is as a defense against herbivores. It also minimizes competition for space. On the other hand, it has a disadvantage when competition for light is taken in to account.

CHAPTER 13
CORAL REEFS

Chapter Summary

Chapter 13 highlights coral reefs, the richest and oldest of marine ecosystems. The material covered is guaranteed to draw students' attention to some important and timely issues, from nutrient cycling to human intrusion into the marine environment.

Reef-building organisms are surveyed first, with an emphasis on the morphology, life history, and nutrition of reef corals. A box includes information on the reproduction of corals. The role of other reef builders, particularly coralline algae, is also discussed. The effect of physical and chemical factors (light, temperature, sediments, salinity, and pollution) is integrated into the discussion. The dramatic example of Kaneohe Bay in Hawaii is used to illustrate the effect of eutrophication brought about by sewage pollution.

The types and origins of coral reefs are outlined next. We use the help of numerous illustrations especially designed for the chapter. Our discussion of the origin of coral reefs centers on Darwin's theory of atoll formation. It should be pointed out that no mention is made of the glacial control theory, which has been thoroughly invalidated by now.

The core of the chapter deals with the ecology of coral reef communities. We have placed particular attention on the discussion of what makes coral reefs unique rather than simply describing the major components of the community. The trophic significance of coral reefs is discussed by examining the recycling of nutrients, nitrogen fixation, the role of zooxanthellae, and the importance of mucus. The many interactions in the community are assessed by looking at competition for space among corals and competition for various resources among fishes. Predation of corals is examined by using the crown-ofthorns plague as an example. Grazing and symbiotic associations complete our review of fascinating interactions.

Audiovisual Material

Videos and Films:
1. Cities of Coral (VHS, videodisc; 60 min., color; Frey Scientific, P.O. Box 8101, Mansfield, OH 44901-8101; (800) 225-3739). A general introduction to life in coral reefs in the Caribbean. From the Nova series.
2. Coral Atoll Biology (VHS, 20 min., color; 50-slide set, filmstrip; Frey Scientific, P.O. Box 8101, Mansfield, OH 44901-8101; (800) 225-3739). Origin of coral atolls and general features of its plant and animal life.
3. The Great Barrier Reef (VHS, 60 min., color; Films for the Humanities and Sciences, P.O. Box 2053, Princeton, NJ 08543; (800) 257-5126). A general survey of life in the Great Barrier Reef.
4. Ecology of the Coral Reef (VHS, 28 min., color; Films for the Humanities and Sciences, P.O. Box 2053, Princeton, NJ 08543; (800) 257-5126). An examination of the many factors that threaten coral reefs. From the Man and the Biosphere series.
5. Within the Coral Wall (VHS, 60 min., color; Carolina Biological Supply, 2700 York Rd., Burlington, NC 27215; (800) 334-5551). Life in the Great Barrier Reef.
6. Cloud Over the Coral Reef (16 mm, 30 min., color; Moonlight Productions, 2243 Old Middlefield Way, Mountain View, CA 94043). An outdated but still useful account of the effect of sewage pollution in Kaneohe Bay, Hawaii.

Slides and Filmstrips:
1. Coral Reefs (20-slide set, filmstrip; Educational Images, P.O. Box 3456, Elmira, NY 14905; (800) 527-4264).
2. Algal Symbiosis (10-slide set, filmstrip; Educational Images, P.O. Box 3456, Elmira, NY 14905; (800) 527-4264).
3. Behavioral Significance of Coloration Among Reef Fishes (20-slide set; Educational Images, P.O. Box 3456, Elmira, NY 14905; (800) 527-4264).
4. Coral Reef Fish (20-slide set; JLM Visuals, 1208 Bridge St., Grafton, WI 53024-1946; (414) 377-7775, FAX (414) 377-7750).
5. The Ecology of Coral Reefs (filmstrip; Ward's, P.O. Box 92912, Rochester, NY 14692; (800) 962-2660).
6. Exploring the Coral Reef (110-slide set; Ward's, P.O. Box 92912, Rochester, NY 14692; (800) 962-2660).
7. Focus on the Sea—The Chain of Life (83-slide set on the ecology of coral reefs; Ward's, P.O. Box 92912, Rochester, NY 14692; (800) 962-2660).
8. The Atlantic Coral Reefs (69-slide set; Ward's, P.O. Box 92912, Rochester, NY 14692; (800) 962-2660).

Software
1. Coral Reefs and Their Residents (Apple; Educational Images, P.O. Box 3456, Elmira, NY 14905; (800) 527-4264). Types of corals and coral reefs; basic principles of the biology of coral reefs.
2. Coral Reef Stratification (Mac; W.C. Brown, 2460 Kerper Blvd., Dubuque, IA 52001; (800) 553-4920).

Answers to Thought Questions
1. What factors might account for the fact that the vast majority of atolls occur in the Indian and Pacific oceans and that atoll are rare in the Atlantic?

The movement of lithospheric plates over stationary "hot spots" over most of the Indian and Pacific oceans has created several chains of undersea volcanoes and islands far from freshwater runoff and silt from land. Students should be referred to the map in figure 2.11. Atolls eventually developed in many of these chains. No such stationary hot spots occur in the Atlantic. The box, "Hot Spots and the Creation of the Hawaiian Islands," reviews the steps in the formation of island chains from hot spots.

2. Scientists predict that the ocean will get warmer and the sea level will rise as a result of the greenhouse effect described in Chapter 17 (see "Living in a Greenhouse: Our Warming Earth"). How might this affect coral reefs?

If sea level rises faster than the upward growth of coral, many low-lying coral islands and keys around the world may become submerged. It has been predicted that island nations such as the Maldives and the Marshall Islands may disappear altogether. Submerged coral reefs that can't keep up with the rise of sea level may be doomed if not enough light reaches them.

3. There are only a few reefs off the northeast coast of Brazil (see map in figure 13.10), even though it lies in the tropics. How would you explain this?

The Amazon River, whose freshwater plume extends hundreds of miles offshore, restricts the development of reef corals. Water from the Amazon also brings sediment particles that limits coral growth.

CHAPTER 14
LIFE NEAR THE SURFACE

Chapter Outline

The Organisms of the Epipelagic
    The Plankton: A New Understanding
    The Phytoplankton
    The Zooplankton
        Protozoan Zooplankton
        Copepods
        Other crustaceans
        Non-Crustacean Zooplankton
        Meroplankton
    The Nekton
Living in the Epipelagic
    Staying Afloat
        Increased Resistance
        Increased Buoyancy
        The Floaters
    Predators and Their Prey
        Sense Organs
        Coloration and Camouflage
        Swimming: The Need for Speed
        Vertical Migration
Epipelagic Food Webs
    Trophic Levels and Energy Flow
    The Microbial Loop
    Patterns of Production
        Light Limitation
        Nutrients
        Seasonal Patterns
        Upwelling and Productivity
        Geographic Patterns
    The El Niño–Southern Oscillation
Box: *Red Tides*
Box: *Swimming Machines*

Chapter Summary

Chapter 14 deals with the surface layer, or epipelagic zone, of the marine environment, a most important and extensive portion of our planet. The chapter covers a considerable amount of material. This, however, is a result of our strategy of including basic material, such as upwelling and El Niño, where it is biologically relevant. Instructors may in fact opt to use Chapter 14 as a starting point of their survey of the marine environment.

The chapter opens with a description of the most important groups of epipelagic phytoplankton, zooplankton, and nekton. These sections have been rewritten in the second edition. It also includes a helpful new table that summarizes the classification of plankton. Basic morphological characteristics and feeding habits are stresses. The discussion includes some recent information on the importance of nanoplankton in primary productivity. A box on red tides complements the information on phytoplankton. It is recommended to refer students to Appendix A, which will help them visualize the relative size of bacteria, plankton, and nekton.

The second section deals with the crucial adaptations of epipelagic organisms. We discuss adaptations for staying afloat within the epipelagic (including an examination of the neuston) and those adaptations involved in finding food and escaping from predators. Adaptations for fast swimming in epipelagic fishes are highlighted in a box.

Food webs in the epipelagic are discussed in the concluding section. We examine the basic patterns of trophic structure and the role of detritus, bacteria, and dissolved organic matter. Primary production and its limiting factors (light, nutrients, seasonal patterns, and upwelling) are then discussed in some detail. The discussion makes use of a novel illustration to help explain upwelling. Extensive coverage is made of the El Niño–Southern Oscillation, a phenomenon much discussed by the media in recent years.

Audiovisual Material

Videos and Films:

1. Gelatinous Zooplankton (3/4 inch video, 16 mm; 17 min., color; 1980; Department of Instructional Development, University of California, Santa Barbara, CA 93106). A survey of zooplankton in their natural habitat.
2. Plankton and the Open Sea (16 mm, 19 min., color; Encyclopedia Britannica, 310 S. Michigan Ave., Chicago, IL 60604; (302) 321-7105). An introduction to the ecology of marine plankton.
3. Face of the Deep (VHS, 58 min., color; Insight Media, 2162 Broadway, New York, NY 10024). Inhabitants of the upper layer of the ocean: the neuston and the Sargasso weed community.
4. Ocean Desert: The Sargasso Sea (VHS, 9 min., color; Films for the Humanities & Sciences, P.O. Box 2053, Princeton, NJ 08543; (800)257-5126). The Sargasso weed community and its ability to thrive in waters poor in nutrients.
5. The Portuguese Man-of-War (VHS, 9 min., color; Films for the Humanities & Sciences, P.O. Box 2053, Princeton, NJ 08543; (800)257-5126). The natural history of Physalia.

Slides and Filmstrips:

1. Marine Phytoplankton (20-slide set; Educational Images, P.O. Box 3456, Elmira, NY 14905; (800) 527-4264).
2. Zooplankton (15-slide set, filmstrip; Educational Images, P.O. Box 3456, Elmira, NY 14905; (800) 527-4264).
3. Plankton Communities (15-slide set, filmstrip; Educational Images, P.O. Box 3456, Elmira, NY 14905; (800) 527-4264).
4. Pelagic Communities (15-slide set, filmstrip; Educational Images, P.O. Box 3456, Elmira, NY 14905; (800) 527-4264).
5. Light and Primary Productivity (20-slide set, filmstrip; Educational Images, P.O. Box 3456, Elmira, NY 14905; (800) 527-4264).
6. Plankton: The Living Sea (6 color film loops on various aspects of the biology of marine plankton; Kalmia, 71 Dudley St., Cambridge, MA 02140; (617) 864-5567).
7. Marine Plankton (filmstrip; Ward's, P.O. Box 92912, Rochester, NY 14692; (800) 962-2660).
8. Marine Plankton (20-slide set; JLM Visuals, 1208 Bridge St., Grafton, WI 53024-1946; (414) 377-7775, FAX (414) 377-7750).

Answers to Thought Questions

1. Plankton are unable to swim effectively and drift about at the mercy of the currents. You might think that the currents would scatter planktonic organisms throughout the oceans, but many species are restricted to particular regions. What mechanisms might allow a species to maintain its characteristic distribution?

The geographic, or horizontal, distribution of plankton is limited by the physical and chemical characteristics of water masses (temperature, nutrients, and salinity). Particular water masses circulate in the form of gyre systems that show little mixing with surrounding masses (see figure 3.20). The plankton in these and other water masses has been fund to be relatively uniform and have been considered as specific biotic provinces. Biotic factors (food limitations and predation) may be suggested as factors that influence this patchy pattern of distribution.

2. Spiny species of diatoms are found both in warm subtropical waters as well as in colder areas. Since warm water is less dense that cold water, would you predict any differences between the spines of warm-water and cold-water individuals? Why?

Spines in widely distributed species of diatoms are longer in warm water than in cold water since the lower density of warm water calls for longer spines to keep cells from sinking.

CHAPTER 15
THE OCEAN DEPTHS

Chapter Outline
The Twilight World
    The Animals of the Mesopelagic
        Zooplankton
        Midwater Fishes
    Adaptations of Midwater Animals
        Feeding and Food Webs
        Vertical Migration and the Deep Scattering Layer
        Sense Organs
        Coloration and Body Shape
        Bioluminescence
        The Oxygen Minimum Layer
The World of Perpetual Darkness
    The Lack of Food
    Sex in the Deep Sea
    Living Under Pressure
The Deep-Ocean Floor
    Feeding in the Deep-Sea Benthos
    The Nature of Life in the Deep Sea
    Bacteria in the Deep Sea
Hot Springs, Cold Seeps, and Dead Bodies
Box: *The Chambered Nautilus*

Chapter Summary
The chapter examines life in the ocean depths below the epipelagic zone: the mesopelagic and the deep sea. It actually comprises the largest but least known environment on earth.

The animals of the mesopelagic are surveyed first. This section includes recent information about these little-known animals. As in previous chapters, we emphasize general morphological features and feeding habits. The unique adaptations of these animals are outlined next: feeding strategies, vertical migration, sense organs, coloration, and bioluminescence. Included in this section is a concise explanation of the oxygen minimum layer.

Life below the mesopelagic, the deep sea, is examined int he next three sections. A summary of the morphological characteristics of deep-sea animals is followed by a discussion of their most significant adaptations to living under conditions here food is scant, mates are difficult to find in the dark, and pressure is extreme. The benthos of the deep-sea floor is discussed by pointing out adaptations for feeding. The bacteria of the deep-sea floor and their role are examined next. We conclude the discussion of the deep-sea environment with an up-to-date look at hydrothermal vents and their associated fauna.

Integrated into the chapter are photos and illustrations of some of the instruments and techniques used in sampling mesopelagic and deep-sea animals.

Audiovisual Material
Videos and Films:
1. 4000 Meters Under the Sea (VHS, 28 min., color; Films for the Humanities and Sciences, P.O. Box 2053, Princeton, NJ 08543; (800) 257-5126). An expedition uses a deep submersible to investigate life at 4,000 m near the Mariana Trench.
2. The Return of the Child: The Effects of El Niño (VHS, 26 min., color; Films for the Humanities and Sciences, P.O. Box 2053, Princeton, NJ 08543; (800) 257-5126). The causes and effects of ENSO.

3. <u>Dive to the Edge of Creation</u> (16 mm, 59 min., color; National Geographic Society, 17th and M Sts., NW, Washington, DC 20036; (202) 857-7669). A portrait of an expedition to investigate hydrothermal vents.

Slides and Filmstrips:
1. <u>Benthic Communities</u> (15-slide set, filmstrip; Educational Images, P.O. Box 3456, Elmira, NY 14905; (800) 527-4264).
2. <u>Bioluminescence</u> (10-slide set, filmstrip; Educational Images, P.O. Box 3456, Elmira, NY 14905; (800) 527-4264).

<u>Answers to Thought Questions</u>

1. The deep-sea floor has been considered as a potential site for the disposal of toxic and radioactive wastes. What questions about the biology, geology, and chemistry of the deep-sea environment do you think should be answered before such plans are approved?

We should find out more about circulation of water masses in the deep-sea floor, the relative stability of the bottom, possible binding or incorporation of these wastes to organic matter, or even their direct utilization by marine bacteria or larger animals. Migrating animals of those feeding in deep water may transfer these radioactive materials into the food chain and eventually into our food. The danger of radioactive pollution to the marine environment is briefly discussed in the section "Radioactive Wastes" in Chapter 17.

2. How do you think that non-migratory midwater fishes, with their flabby muscles, are able to prey on vertical migrators, which have well-developed muscles?

They may use lures (some of which may be bioluminescent) to attract prey. Some fishes may employ sit-and-wait strategies.

CHAPTER 16
RESOURCES FROM THE SEA

Chapter Outline

The Living Resources of the Sea
  Food from the Sea
    Major Fishing Areas
    Major Food Species
    Optimal Yields and Overfishing
    Managing the Resources
    New Fisheries
    Mariculture
  Marine Life as Items of Commerce and Recreation
    Drugs from the Sea
    Fisheries for Fun
Non-Living Resources from the Sea Floor
  Oil and Gas
  Ocean Mining
Non-Living Resources from Seawater
  Fresh Water
  Minerals
  Energy
Box: *Of Fishes and Seabirds, Fishermen and Chickens*
Box: *Take Two Sponges and Call Me in the Morning*

Chapter Summary

Part IV is a three-chapter, comprehensive examination of the relationship between humans and the sea. We have tried to stimulate in-class discussion by integrating both the positive and the negative, the hopeful solutions as well as the pessimistic predictions. Nevertheless, it won't be difficult for students to get the message that the oceans are not a bottomless source of food and a free-for-all receptacle of garbage.

Chapter 16 discussed our use of marine resources. The first and most extensive of its three sections deals with the use of living resources. We stress food resources and examine the current situation of the world's fisheries including major fishing areas, major food species and fish products, and fishing techniques. The urgent need to manage fisheries to save whatever resources are left is stressed by assessing the problem of overfishing, which has received much attention by the media during the recent years. We then examine the alternatives provided by fisheries management as well as by the utilization of new technologies in the exploitation of new fisheries and in mariculture. The section is supplemented by the extensive use of illustrations, tables that summarize up-to-date information, and a box on the Peruvian anchovy, which highlights the relationships between physical factors, fisheries, and humans. We conclude with a survey of the use of living resources as a source of life-saving drugs, which is covered by a timely box new to the second edition, and in recreation.

The use of resources taken from the sea floor (oil, gas, and minerals) and directly from seawater (freshwater, minerals, and energy) are examined in the last two sections.

Some of the material can be covered with the help of written and/or oral reports by students. The updated list of references at the end of the chapter can serve as a starting point. Another possibility is to assign all students one or more of these articles for class discussion.

Videos and Films:
1. <u>Ocean Resources</u> (VHS, 23 min., color; Films for the Humanities and Sciences, P.O. Box 2053, Princeton, NJ 08543; (800) 257-5126). Examines traditional as well as newer resources from the oceans.
2. <u>Will the Fishing Have to Stop</u>? (3/4 inch video, 16 mm; 31 min., color; Films for the Humanities and Sciences, P.O. Box 2053, Princeton, NJ 08543; (800) 257-5126). Analyzes the modern fisheries and presents possible solutions to the fishing crisis. From the Nova series.
3. <u>Salmon on the Run</u> (VHS, 57 min., color; Films for the Humanities and Sciences, P.O. Box 2053, Princeton, NJ 08543; (800) 257-5126). The effects of salmon ranching on salmon in the wild. From the Nova series.
4. <u>Farmers of the Sea</u> (VHS, 16 mm; 57 min., color; Time-Life Film and Video, 100 Eisenhower Dr., Paramus, NJ 07652). A survey of some of the techniques employed in mariculture. From the Nova series.
5. <u>Aquaculture</u> (VHS, 26 min., color; Films for the Humanities and Sciences, P.O. Box 2053, Princeton, NJ 08543; (800) 257-5126). The practice and consequences of mariculture around the world.
6. <u>The Frontier of Medicine</u> (VHS, 27 min., color; Films for the Humanities and Sciences, P.O. Box 2053, Princeton, NJ 08543; (800) 257-5126). The use of marine organisms to help understand biological phenomena and to obtain drugs.
7. <u>Drugs from the Sea</u> (VHS, 26 min., color; Films for the Humanities and Sciences, P.O. Box 2053, Princeton, NJ 08543; (800) 257-5126). The testing of drugs obtained from marine organisms.

Slides and Filmstrips:
1. <u>Fisheries and Mariculture</u> (20-slide set, filmstrip; Educational Images, P.O. Box 3456, Elmira, NY 14905; (800) 527-4264).
2. <u>Farming the Sea</u> (20-slide set; Educational Images, P.O. Box 3456, Elmira, NY 14905; (800) 527-4264).
3. <u>Restoration of the American Shad</u> (20-slide set; Educational Images, P.O. Box 3456, Elmira, NY 14905; (800) 527-4264).
4. <u>Who Owns the Oceans</u>? (filmstrip; Educational Images, P.O. Box 3456, Elmira, NY 14905; (800) 527-4264).
5. <u>The Oceans: A Key to Our Future</u> (5 filmstrips on marine resources; Ward's, P.O. Box 92912, Rochester, NY 14692; (800) 962-2660).
6. <u>Aquaculture</u> (40-slide set; JLM Visuals, 1208 Bridge St., Grafton, WI 53024-1946; (414) 377-7775, FAX (414) 377-7750).

Answers to Thought Questions

1. It is discovered that for the last three years the annual catches of a commercially important fish have been above the maximum sustainable yield. One option is to decrease the fishing effort by decreasing the number of fishermen. This, however, would cause unemployment in a region where unemployment is already high. What other options might ensure a lower fishing effort? How could they be carried out? There are several ways to manage a fishery. The catch can be reduced by using a different type of net (as illustrated in figure 16.12), by using a different but less efficient fishing method, and/or using a smaller number of boats or fishermen. If the number of boats is kept constant in order to prevent the unemployment of fishermen, the boats can be required to use less powerful engines. A fishing season may be implemented. Another possibility would be to reduce the catch and utilize a by-catch that the fishermen are currently throwing away. These changes would be carried out a result of a mutual agreement among the fishermen, by legislation, and/or by an international agreement.

2. The mariculture of many food species is expensive, and often only high-priced species are raised. This type of mariculture is of little help to the poor nations where food is needed the most. What measures and new developments might help increase the value of mariculture to these poor nations?

One way of decreasing the cost of mariculture is to develop inexpensive, local techniques such as the use of simple fish ponds or floating cages along the coast, as in the example illustrated in figure 16.15. At the same time we should develop the farming of new food species that can be inexpensively raised under these conditions. Diets are difficult to change so this may involve the use of marketing strategies.
3. It has been suggested that cheap electricity generated from tides, waves, or currents could be used to pump nutrient-rich water from the deep. The water could then be used to grow algae to feed the larvae of farmed fishes and invertebrates. How else could this energy be used to decrease the costs of mariculture? The energy can be used to regulate the temperature of the water for optimal growth of the fish being farmed. This is particularly important in the growth of larval or juvenile stages.

CHAPTER 17
IMPACT OF HUMANS ON THE MARINE ENVIRONMENT

Chapter Outline

Pollution
    Oil
        Sources
        Effects on Marine Life
    Sewage
        Raw Sewage
        Sewage Treatment and Sludge
        Alternatives
    Synthetic Chemicals
        Chlorinated Hydrocarbons
        PCBs
    Heavy Metals
        Mercury
        Other Heavy Metals
    Thermal Pollution
    Solid Waste
    Radioactive Wastes
Modification and Destruction of Habitats
    Estuaries
    Mangrove Forests
    Coral Reefs
Threatened and Endangered Species
    The Case of the Whales
    Other Marine Species Facing Extinction
Alien Species
Conserving and Enhancing the Environment
    Conservation
    Restoration of Habitats
    Artificial Reefs

Box: *Living in a Greenhouse: Our Warming Earth*
Box: *Sand on the Run, or What to Do with Our Shrinking Beaches*
Box: *Ten Simple Things We Can Do to Save the Oceans*

Chapter Summary

The chapter examines the impact of humans on the marine environment, a most pressing subject that should be thoroughly covered in class.

The first and most extensive section deals with the types, sources, and effects of marine pollutants. Emphasis is given to oil, sewage, and synthetic chemicals, but pollution by heavy metals, thermal effluents, solid waste, and radioactive material is also discussed. We have tried to discuss any available alternatives or options to the release of pollutants into the water.

Other examples of the effects of human intrusion are covered next. The modification and destruction of habitats such as estuaries and coral reefs is explored. Reference should be made to the box on the significance of biodiversity in Chapter 9, which is new to the second edition. Threatened and endangered species are covered next by using whaling and the predicament of whales as the primary example. Effects as varied as the use of drift nets, shark fishing, and shell collecting are brought into the discussion. Also analyzed are the effects of alien species. An expanded, timely box on global warming and its possible effect on sea level is included in the second edition.

The last section deals with efforts to conserve and enhance the marine environment. It explores ways to reverse the degradation of the marine environment by conservation efforts, coastal management, the restoration of habitats, and the building of artificial reefs. The question of coastal management and beach erosion is discussed in a box. Another box, "Ten Simple Things We Can Do to Save the Oceans," closes the chapter with the optimistic message that we can all make the difference by getting involved and keeping informed.

As in Chapter 16, direct student involvement and discussion can be encouraged by assigning them one or more of the articles included at the end of the chapter.

Audiovisual Material
Videos and Films:

1. Heading for Shore: The Struggle to Save America's Coasts (VHS, 16 mm; 29 min., color; Umbrella Films, 60 Blake Road, Brookline, MA 02146; (617) 277-6639). A look at the problems faced by coastal areas by examining three case studies on Atlantic, Gulf, and Pacific locations.
2. Inherit the Seas: America's Marine Sanctuaries (VHS, 16 mm; 30 min., color; Umbrella Films, 60 Blake Road, Brookline, MA 02146; (617) 277-6639). The role played by marine sanctuaries.
3. The Ocean Sink (VHS, 29 min., color; Films for the Humanities and Sciences, P.O. Box 2053, Princeton, NJ 08543; (800) 257-5126). The effect of industrial wastes on marine life.
4. Seas Under Siege (VHS, 56 min., color; Films for the Humanities and Sciences, P.O. Box 2053, Princeton, NJ 08543; (800) 257-5126). A comprehensive survey of sources and effects of marine pollutants.
5. The Effects of Water Pollution (VHS, 19 min., color; Films for the Humanities and Sciences, P.O. Box 2053, Princeton, NJ 08543; (800) 257-5126). The effects of pollution on marine life. From The Fragile Planet series.
6. PCBs in the Food Chain (VHS, 18 min., color; Films for the Humanities and Sciences, P.O. Box 2053, Princeton, NJ 08543; (800) 257-5126). How PCBs accumulate in higher levels of marine food chains. From The Fragile Planet series.
7. Marine Detectives (VHS, 15 min., color; Films for the Humanities and Sciences, P.O. Box 2053, Princeton, NJ 08543; (800) 257-5126). Marine environmental issues are examined using a case study approach. From the Race to Save the Planet PBS series.
8. Coastal Erosion (VHS, 14 min., color; Films for the Humanities and Sciences, P.O. Box 2053, Princeton, NJ 08543; (800) 257-5126). The coastal defenses in The Netherlands.
9. Marine Pollution (VHS, 30 min., color; Insight Media, 2162 Broadway, New York, NY 10024). The types of marine pollutants and the efforts to control them.
10. Are You Swimming in a Sewer? (VHS, 58 min., color; WGBH TV, 125 Western Ave., Boston, MA 02134; (800) 828-9424). A look at pollution in the oceans. From the Nova series.
11. The Mediterranean Prospect (16 mm, 55 min., color; WGBH TV, 125 Western Ave., Boston, MA 02134; (800) 828-9424). Pollution in the Mediterranean Sea. From the Nova series.
12. Black Tide (16 mm, 58 min., color; WGBH TV, 125 Western Ave., Boston, MA 02134; (800) 828-9424). The Amoco Cadiz oil spill disaster. From the Nova series.
13. Alaska: Crude Awakening (VHS, 47 min., color; Films for the Humanities and Sciences, P.O. Box 2053, Princeton, NJ 08543; (800) 257-5126). The Exxon Valdez oil spill.
14. PCBs in the Food Chain (VHS, 18 min., color; Films for the Humanities and Sciences, P.O. Box 2053, Princeton, NJ 08543; (800) 257-5126). The accumulation of PCBs in marine food chains.
15. Hot Enough For You? (VHS, 16 mm; 60 min., color; Films for the Humanities and Sciences, P.O. Box 2053, Princeton, NJ 08543; (800) 257-5126). A discussion of global warming, including the possible effects on sea level. From the Nova series.

16. <u>After</u> <u>the</u> <u>Warming</u> (VHS, 2 hrs., color; JLM Visuals, 1208 Bridge St., Grafton, WI 53024-1946; (414) 377-7775, FAX (414) 377-7750). A comprehensive look at global warming, including the possible effects on sea level.

17. <u>Cloud</u> <u>Over</u> <u>the</u> <u>Coral</u> <u>Reef</u> (16 mm, 30 min., color; Moonlight Productions, 2243 Old Middlefield Way, Mountain View, CA 94043). An outdated but still useful account of the effects of sewage pollution on Kaneohe Bay, Hawaii.

18. <u>The</u> <u>Poisoned</u> <u>Sea</u> (16 mm, 27 min., color; Moonlight Productions, 2243 Old Middlefield Way, Mountain View, CA 94043). The effects of pollution and grazing on southern California kelp forests.

19. <u>Affluent</u> <u>Effluent</u> (VHS, 31 min., color; Carolina Biological Supply, 2700 York Rd., Burlington, NC 27215; (800) 334-5551). The different types of wastewater treatment.

20. <u>Whales</u> <u>and</u> <u>Whaling</u> (16 mm, 25 min., color; Media Guild, 11722 Sorrento Valley Rd., San Diego, CA 92121; (619) 755-9191). An outdated but informative look at the history of whaling and its impact on the survival of whales.

21. <u>Hole</u> <u>in</u> <u>the</u> <u>Sky</u>: <u>The</u> <u>Ozone</u> <u>Layer</u> (VHS, 52 min., color; Films for the Humanities and Sciences, P.O. Box 2053, Princeton, NJ 08543; (800) 257-5126). The potentially harmful effects of the depletion of the ozone layer.

22. <u>The</u> <u>Greenhouse</u> <u>Effect</u> (VHS, 26 min., color; Films for the Humanities and Sciences, P.O. Box 2053, Princeton, NJ 08543; (800) 257-5126). A look at the relationship between sun radiation and CO_2 levels in the earth's atmosphere. From the <u>Climate</u> <u>and</u> <u>Man</u> series.

23. <u>Global</u> <u>Warming</u> (VHS, 26 min., color; Films for the Humanities and Sciences, P.O. Box 2053, Princeton, NJ 08543; (800) 257-5126). A comprehensive look at the causes and potential effects of global warming. From the <u>Climate</u> <u>and</u> <u>Man</u> series.

24. <u>The</u> <u>Greenhouse</u> <u>Effect</u> and <u>Global</u> <u>Climate</u>: <u>Jessica</u> <u>Tuchman</u> <u>Mathews</u> (VHS, 30 min., color; Films for the Humanities and Sciences, P.O. Box 2053, Princeton, NJ 08543; (800) 257-5126). An interview with a biochemist/biophysicist discussing global warming.

25. <u>Assessing</u> <u>our</u> <u>Planet's</u> <u>Health</u>: <u>Lester</u> <u>Brown</u> (VHS, 30 min., color; Films for the Humanities and Sciences, P.O. Box 2053, Princeton, NJ 08543; (800) 257-5126). Another view of global warming.

26. <u>The</u> <u>Greenhouse</u> <u>Effect</u> (videodisc; Media Design Associates, P.O. Box 3189, Boulder, CO 80307-3189; (800) 228-8854). The causes and effects of global warming.

Software

1. <u>Ocean</u> <u>Pollution</u> (CD-ROM; W.C. Brown, 2460 Kerper Blvd., Dubuque, IA 52001; (800) 553-4920). Includes more than 100 photographs with descriptive captions.

2. <u>Water</u> <u>Pollution</u> (Apple, Mac, IBM; EME, P.O. Box 2805, Danbury, CT 06813; (800) 848-2050). Interactive simulation where students manipulate variables such at the type of waste and dumping rate.

3. <u>Hothouse</u> <u>Planet</u> (Apple, Mac, IBM; EME, P.O. Box 2805, Danbury, CT 06813; (800) 848-2050). A system where the effect of greenhouse gases on global temperature and sea level are examined.

4. <u>Pollute</u>: <u>Impact</u> <u>of</u> <u>Water</u> <u>Pollutants</u> (Apple, IBM; Educational Images, P.O. Box 3456, Elmira, NY 14905; (800) 527-4264). Type and impact of water pollutants.

<u>Answers</u> <u>to</u> <u>Thought</u> <u>Questions</u>

1. Wastes from duck farms used to wash into two shallow-water bays on Long Island, New York. The wastes, rich in nutrients such as nitrate and phosphate, polluted the water. What do you suppose was the immediate effect of the pollutants? Can you speculate on the likely effects to the commercially valuable shellfish of the area?

The immediate effect of enrichment, or eutrophication, of the water was to stimulate the growth of algae, which depleted the oxygen dissolved in the water. Depletion of oxygen on the bottom triggered the development of anaerobic conditions and an accumulation of toxic hydrogen sulfide in the sediment. This adversely affected the shellfish. Similar effects of eutrophication in the marine environment are outlined in the section "The Kaneohe Bay Story" in Chapter 13.

2. It is found that a chemical present in effluents coming from a factory is being stored in the tissues of herring, a plankton-feeding fish. What type of observations and possible experiments would you suggest to find out if the chemical is biodegradable? What is the significance of finding out if the chemical is biodegradable or not?

Experiments can be carried out with herring (or a similar fish) kept under artificial conditions in the laboratory or in isolated ponds. Measured amounts of a pollutant can be given as part of their food, assuming this can be done with planktonic food. The pollutant can be considered non-biodegradable if it accumulates in the tissues, especially in body fat, of the fish. It would be very important to find out if the pollutant is biodegradable since biological magnification may increase its concentration in the food chain. Herring, or any other small, plankton-feeding fish, is the food of larger fishes that are consumed by humans.

3. Tourism and its effects (for example, pollution from hotels and the impact of boats and tourists on fragile habitats) often clash with conservation efforts. Sometimes, however, tourism can help. The economic impact of banning the hunting of harp seals in eastern Canada has been compensated for in part by the influx of tourists that now come to see the seals. Can you think of other examples? What recommendations can you make to minimize the impact of tourism on unspoiled marine environments?

Students may bring in examples of nature-oriented tours to protected coasts or underwater parks in the Galápagos Islands, the Caribbean, the Great Barrier Reef, and other areas. Impact by tourism must be kept to a minimum by establishing protected marine reserves and parks and restricting the number of tourists that may visit them, the specific locations they can visit, and the places where they stay overnight. Education of visiting tourists and the public in general must be an essential objective of these reserved and parks.

CHAPTER 18
THE OCEANS AND HUMAN AFFAIRS

Chapter Outline
Oceans as Barriers and Avenues
Oceans and Cultures
Oceans and Recreation
Prospects for the Future
Box: *Marine Archeology*

Chapter Summary
Chapter 18 can be best described as an essay that reflects on the many ways the marine environment has affected human cultures. We aim to integrate all the knowledge that non-science students have gained about the marine environment with their particular fields of interest, from the humanities to business. We suggest assigning the chapter for class discussion at the end of the course, an idea successfully tested by users of the first edition.

The chapter first looks at the oceans through the eyes of history: as a medium that initially served as a barrier to the diffusion of cultures but one that eventually served as a crucial avenue for cultural exchange. It remains today as a link of world economies, and as such one that business people rely upon. The impact of the ocean on shaping cultures is examined by briefly describing examples of maritime cultures that anthropology and sociology students may find intriguing. A box on marine archeology looks at how the ocean can proved valuable information about our past.

The influence of the oceans on less tangible aspects of human endeavors—the plastic arts, literature, and music — is also brought into the discussion. More concrete activities that regularly affect the lives of millions, that of marine recreation, are also discussed. We conclude the chapter (and the book) by reflecting on what lies ahead in the future of the world oceans.

Audiovisual Material
Videos and Films:
1. Hunters of the Seal (3/4 inch video, 16 mm; 30 min., color; WGBH TV, 125 Western Ave., Boston, MA 02134; (800) 828-9424). The traditional and the new in the life of the Netsilik Eskimos of Canada. From the Nova series.
2. Diving for Roman Plunder (3/4 inch video; 60 min., color; Coronet/MTI Film and Video, 108 Wilmont Rd., Deerfield, IL 60015; (800) 621-2131). The exploration of a 2,000-year old shipwreck off the coast of Greece. A Jacques Cousteau film.

Answers to Thought Questions
1. Most marine cultures are either long gone or have been radically modified by others. Which elements of a rapidly changing maritime culture do you predict would be the first to disappear? Which would tend to remain unchanged the longest?
It is now suspected hat some of the most "attractive" elements of modern culture (heavily advertised clothing articles, convenience foods, sports, toys, and so forth) will be the first ones to penetrate into the relatively untouched culture and thus replace some or all of the indigenous counterparts. The less superficial elements of a culture (such as language and religion) would be expected to be more resistant, but not immune, to change.
2. The Third United Nations Conference on the Law of the Sea made no provisions for Antarctica. Some of the land is probably rich in resources like oil, so the eventual exploitation of the land is probably inevitable. Several nations have already established claims, sometimes overlapping each other, to sections of the continent. How would you deal with these claims? Would you give first preference to nations, like Argentina or New Zealand, that claim geographic proximity to the continent or to those, like Norway or Britain, that arrived at the claimed land first? How can resources be exploited if it is decided that the land does not belong to any particular nations?

This is another question with no particular answer, one perfect for discussion. The 1991 treaty signed by the United States and 30 other nations that bans mining and oil exploration in Antarctica for fifty years should be mentioned in the discussion.

Test Item File

About MicroTest III

This Test Item File is available on MicroTest III, a complete testing system free to adopters of this text.

Instructors who use MicroTest III find that this convenient system saves hours of test preparation time. Using the program yourself requires access to a personal computer that has DOS or Windows (3-1/2 inch only) capabilities with a 5-1/4 or 3-1/2 inch diskette drive, or a Macintosh. Diskettes are available through your local WCB sales representative or by phoning Educational Services at (800) 331-2111.

As another option, you may use WCB's convenient call-in/mail-in/FAX service to generate tests. To use this service, select the questions to include in the customized test, then simply call (800) 258-2385, mail to (Judi David/ Wm. C. Brown Publishers/2460 Kerper Blvd./Dubuque, IA 52001), or FAX (319-589-2955) your request to WCB. Within two working days of receiving your order WCB sends, by first-class mail or FAX, a test master, a student answer sheet, and an answer key for fast and easy grading.

For more information about MicroTest III, please contact your local WCB sales representative or call Judi David at (800) 258-2385.

Using the Test Item File with MicroTest III

The questions that follow are contained on the Test Item File diskette(s) included with the MicroTest III software. Following are some general notes about the Test Item File software:

1. On tests produced with MicroTest III, illustrations automatically print with the questions, those questions that use illustrations can show either the illustration itself or the filename the illustration is stored in.

2. If this test item file contains matching questions, the answers are scrambled.

3. If these test items are followed by a keyword or difficulty level, MicroTest II can select questions using these references as criteria. MicroTest III can also select all questions or select by odd or even numbering.

4. A full screen Text Editor can be used to modify the text of existing questions, or to create your own questions.

5. Tests can be transferred to ASCII format to be used by word processing or page layout programs.

CHAPTER 1
THE SCIENCE OF MARINE BIOLOGY

1. The <u>Challenger</u> expedition made collections of marine organisms:
   a. around the world
   b. in the Pacific Ocean only
   c. in the Atlantic Ocean only
   d. in the Mediterranean Sea only
   e. in the North Sea only

2. The first marine laboratory in the world was established in:
   a. Russia
   b. England
   c. France
   d. Italy
   e. Japan

3. The first marine laboratory established in the U.S. was:
   a. Friday Harbor Marine Laboratory in Washington
   b. Scripps Institution of Oceanography in California
   c. Marine Biological Laboratory at Woods Hole, Massachusetts
   d. Smithsonian Institution in Washington
   e. Hopkins Marine Station in California

4. Charles Darwin, who proposed the theory of evolution, was actually a marine biologist who specialized in:
   a. whales
   b. fishes
   c. marine birds
   d. barnacles
   e. oysters

5. A technological development that was a direct development of World War II:
   a. scuba
   b. research vessels
   c. nets
   d. marine laboratories
   e. sonar

6. The scientific method can be best described as:
   a. undertaking of experiments in laboratories
   b. using of induction and deduction
   c. collecting data in the field
   d. procedures used to learn about our world
   e. steps used to obtain observations

7. The factors that might affect observations are called:
   a. controls
   b. variables
   c. experiments
   d. hypotheses
   e. inductive observations

8. A control can be best defined as:
   a. a variable that is kept constant in an experiment
   b. an experiment where the final results are known ahead of time
   c. a hypothesis that regulates the results of an experiment
   d. an experiment that is undertaken both in the field and in the laboratory
   e. a variable that changes during the course of an experiment

9. A marine biologist observes that mako sharks, sardines, and salmon leap out of the water. An example of induction from these observations is:
   a. only some fishes can leap out of the water
   b. all fishes leap out of the water
   c. fishes leap out of the water to escape from predators
   d. flatfishes can leap out of the water since they live on the bottom
   e. leaping out of the water is often used in feeding

10. From the general statement "All fishes lay eggs," the following statement results from deduction:
    a. since tuna are fish, tuna lay eggs
    b. since tuna are fish, tuna swim
    c. egg laying is beneficial to fishes
    d. tuna must lay their eggs in deep water
    e. since fishes are marine, tuna lay eggs

11. An example of a hypothesis that is not a valid scientific hypothesis because it cannot be proven false:
    a. the earth is flat
    b. the sun revolves around the earth
    c. organisms similar to deep-water marine worms live in the center of the earth
    d. the deepest spot on the ocean is off the coast of a volcanic island
    e. whales listen to sound

12. An experiment can be best described as:
    a. a set of observations that become a hypothesis
    b. obtaining data from the field
    c. an artificially created situation to test a hypothesis
    d. controlling a particular factor in the field
    e. making observations from naturally occurring events

13. Science is limited since it cannot:
    a. predict the future
    b. make judgments about ethics, values, and morality
    c. arrive at fundamental truths
    d. provide information that can be applied to real life
    e. provide exceptions for negative evidence

14. One of the following is outside the realm of science:
    a. observations made using extrasensory perception (ESP)
    b. data collected from an experiment
    c. data collected from the field
    d. anything that can be obtained by our senses
    e. observations made by from satellites

15. Scientific knowledge is ultimately traced to:
    a. hypotheses
    b. inductions
    c. deductions
    d. theories
    e. observations

CHAPTER 2
THE SEA FLOOR

1. One of the following is <u>not</u> one of the world's major ocean basins:
   a. Atlantic Ocean
   b. Arctic Ocean
   c. Indian Ocean
   d. Antarctic Ocean
   e. Pacific Ocean

2. The world's smallest and shallowest ocean:
   a. Atlantic Ocean
   b. Arctic Ocean
   c. Indian Ocean
   d. Antarctic Ocean
   e. Pacific Ocean

3. The world's largest and deepest ocean:
   a. Atlantic Ocean
   b. Arctic Ocean
   c. Indian Ocean
   d. Antarctic Ocean
   e. Pacific Ocean

4. Oceanographers often use the name "Southern Ocean" to refer to the body of water:
   a. around Antarctica
   b. in the South Pacific
   c. south of the North Sea
   d. south of Japan
   e. around the southern tip of Africa

5. Density is:
   a. the mass of a substance per unit volume
   b. a measure of weight
   c. the mass of a substance multiplied by its percentage volume of water
   d. a measure of volume
   e. the volume occupied by a particular substance in relation to that of water

6. There is evidence that the earth and the rest of the solar system formed about:
   a. 5 million years ago
   b. 1 billion years ago
   c. 4.5 billion years ago
   d. 10.5 billion years ago
   e. 10 million years ago

7. The solid layer of the earth found below the crust is called the:
   a. inner core
   b. mantle
   c. inner crust
   d. outer core
   e. oceanic crust

8. The earth's magnetic field is thought to be caused by movements in which of the earth's layers?
    a. inner core
    b. outer core
    c. oceanic crust
    d. mantle
    e. continental crust
9. The thinnest layer of the earth is the:
    a. inner core
    b. outer core
    c. crust
    d. mantle
10. Which of the following is <u>not</u> true of oceanic crust?
    a. it is thinner than continental crust
    b. it is denser than continental crust
    c. it is geologically younger than continental crust
    d. it lies below sea level
    e. it consists mostly of granite
11. Which of the following is <u>not</u> true of mid-ocean ridges?
    a. earthquakes and volcanoes are associated with them
    b. the sediments get thinner as one moves away from them
    c. the rock on the sea floor is older as one moves away from them
    d. sea-floor spreading is associated with them
    e. all are interconnected
12. Lithospheric plates:
    a. only contain continental crust
    b. only contain oceanic crust
    c. collide with one another at the mid-ocean ridge
    d. float on the upper mantle
    e. are directly connected with the inner core of the earth
13. Trenches are formed where:
    a. a plate is lifted by another
    b. a plate moves above another
    c. a plate splits and opens up
    d. sea-floor spreading takes place
    e. a plate sinks beneath another
14. The process by which a lithospheric plate descends into the mantle is called:
    a. continental drift
    b. induction
    c. sea-floor spreading
    d. subduction
    e. faulting
15. The friction zone along the shear boundary between two lithospheric plates is called a:
    a. fault
    b. rift
    c. trench
    d. mid-ocean ridge
    e. sea-floor spreading

16. An example of an island arch along a trench:
    a. Aleutian Islands
    b. Hawaiian Islands
    c. Australia
    d. California
    e. South America
17. Which in not a type of lithospheric plate boundary?
    a. shear boundary
    b. continental margin
    c. trench
    d. mid-ocean ridge
18. The vast single ocean present about 200 million years ago is called:
    a. Sinus Borealis
    b. Pangaea
    c. Tethys
    d. Panthalassa
    e. Gondwana
19. Lithogenous sediments are those that come from:
    a. plants
    b. living organisms in general
    c. deep-water volcanoes
    d. erosion of land
    e. corals
20. The outer edge of the continental margin is the:
    a. shelf break
    b. continental slope
    c. continental rise
    d. edge of the abyssal plain
    e. continental edge
21. The steepest part of the continental margin is known as the:
    a. shelf break
    b. continental slope
    c. continental rise
    d. edge of the abyssal plain
    e. continental edge
22. The shallow part of the continental margin that is closer to land is known as:
    a. shelf break
    b. continental slope
    c. continental rise
    d. edge of the abyssal plain
    e. continental shelf
23. The west coast of South America is an active margin. As such, it is characterized by all of the following except:
    a. earthquakes
    b. volcanoes
    c. wide continental shelf
    d. steep and rocky shorelines
    e. steep continental slope

24. The east coast of the United States is a passive margin characterized by:
    a. mountains along the coast
    b. steep and rocky shorelines
    c. narrow continental shelf
    d. offshore trench
    e. gentle continental slope
25. Black smokers form as a result of the accumulation of:
    a. deep-water animals
    b. lava
    c. biogenous sediments
    d. minerals
    e. material released from the formation of trenches

CHAPTER 3
CHEMICAL AND PHYSICAL FEATURES OF THE WORLD OCEAN

1. Hydrogen bonds in water molecules are formed between:
   a. hydrogen atoms of adjacent molecules
   b. oxygen atoms of adjacent molecules
   c. hydrogen and oxygen atoms of adjacent molecules
   d. two hydrogen atoms of the same molecule
   e. two oxygen atoms of the same molecule
2. The process by which water molecules go from liquid to gaseous phase is known as:
   a. condensation
   b. melting
   c. sublimation
   d. evaporation
   e. crystallization
3. Water molecules in a gaseous state:
   a. move faster than those in a liquid state
   b. move slower than those in a solid state
   c. form more hydrogen bonds than in a liquid state
   d. are closer together than in a liquid state
   e. form crystals as temperature increases
4. A temperature of 4°C indicates:
   a. boiling point of water
   b. maximum density of water
   c. freezing point of water
   d. sublimation point of water
   e. condensation point of water
5. Hydrogen bonds:
   a. lower the heat capacity of water
   b. cause ice to melt at a lower temperature
   c. make ice less dense than water
   d. lower the boiling point of water
   e. do not affect the heat capacity of water at all
6. Which ions comprises about 85% of the solutes in seawater?
   a. magnesium and sulfate
   b. sodium and chloride
   c. calcium and carbonate
   d. potassium and chloride
   e. calcium and sulfate
7. The salinity of water is expressed in:
   a. percentage per thousand liters of water
   b. total weight per pound
   c. percentage per liter
   d. parts per thousand
   e. percentage per thousand

8. The rule of constant proportions expresses that:
   a. salinity varies with geographical location
   b. the percentage of sodium varies with depth
   c. the percentage of chlorine varies with geographical location
   d. salinity varies depending on the season
   e. the relative concentration of ions does not change
9. Salinity of seawater increases:
   a. with an increase in rain
   b. near the mouth of rivers
   c. around ice as it melts in spring
   d. with a decrease in depth
   e. as evaporation increases
10. Which of these bodies of water has the lowest salinity?
    a. Baltic Sea
    b. Red Sea
    c. Atlantic Ocean along the Equator
    d. Pacific Ocean along the Equator
    e. the middle of the Indian Ocean
11. The Secchi disk is used to measure:
    a. the type of light that is absorbed by water
    b. how much light penetrates through the water column
    c. how salinity varies with depth
    d. the relationship between temperature and salinity
    e. the amount of oxygen in the water
12. Which type of light penetrates the least in water?
    a. blue
    b. green
    c. yellow
    d. violet
    e. red
13. Pressure increases with depth by adding one atmosphere of pressure for every:
    a. 10 meters of depth
    b. 50 meters of depth
    c. 100 meters of depth
    d. 500 meters of depth
    e. none of the above, pressure depends on the temperature of the water
14. The Coriolis effect is the direct result of one of the following:
    a. temperature
    b. gravitational pull of the sun
    c. ocean currents
    d. rotation of the earth
    e. wind
15. The factor that most affects wind patterns in the atmosphere of the earth:
    a. depth of the sea
    b. clouds
    c. temperature
    d. volcanoes
    e. gravitational pull of sun and moon

16. Trade winds:
    a. are unaffected by the Coriolis effect
    b. approach the Equator at a 90 degrees angle
    c. develop between 30 degrees north and 30 degrees south
    d. move north in the Northern Hemisphere
    e. change direction depending on ocean currents
17. Gyres are:
    a. large circular systems of surface currents
    b. affected by the Coriolis effect only in the Northern Hemisphere
    c. extend along the Equator
    d. extend over Antarctica
    e. are found only in the Pacific Ocean
18. The major surface currents of the oceans rotate counterclockwise in the:
    a. Northern Hemisphere only
    b. Southern Hemisphere only
    c. in both hemispheres
    d. in the Atlantic Ocean only
    e. in the Pacific Ocean only
19. A cold current flows almost into the Equator along the:
    a. Atlantic coast of North America
    b. Atlantic coast of South America
    c. Pacific coast of Australia
    d. Pacific coast of Asia
    e. Pacific coast of South America
20. The highest part of a wave is called the:
    a. trough
    b. period
    c. minimum height
    d. wavelength
    e. crest
21. The distance between two adjacent wave crests is the:
    a. period
    b. fetch
    c. amplitude
    d. wavelength
    e. height
22. Tides are caused by:
    a. gravitational attraction of the moon
    b. gravitational attraction of the sun
    c. gravitational attraction of the moon and the sun
    d. ocean currents that affect the particular area
    e. ocean currents that affect the world ocean
23. A full tidal cycle lasts:
    a. 12 hours
    b. 12 hours, 50 minutes
    c. 24 hours
    d. 24 hours, 50 minutes
    e. 48 hours

24. Mixed semidiurnal tides are characterized by:
    a. two daily high tides, one higher than the other
    b. one daily high tide
    c. two daily high tides, both of the same approximate height
    d. one daily high tide that is always higher than the high tide of the previous day
    e. two daily high and three daily low tides
25. The main thermocline is located at the zone:
    a. right above the mixed layer
    b. between the warm and cold layers
    c. along the bottom
    d. below the intermediate layer
    e. right at the surface in warm tropical water

CHAPTER 4
THE BUSINESS OF LIFE

1. All of the following are characteristics of living things <u>except</u> one:
   a. grow
   b. produce diseases
   c. reproduce
   d. metabolize
   e. react to the external environment

2. Which is <u>not</u> an organic compound?
   a. water
   b. sugars
   c. proteins
   d. lipids
   e. nucleic acids

3. Glucose is an example of a:
   a. protein
   b. lipid
   c. starch
   d. carbohydrate
   e. hormone

4. One important function of carbohydrates is that they:
   a. form enzymes
   b. are structural molecules
   c. repelling water
   d. store energy
   e. hold genetic information

5. Which of the following organic molecules stores energy, provide insulation and assist in buoyancy?
   a. proteins
   b. carbohydrates
   c. lipids
   d. nucleic acids
   e. amino acids

6. DNA is a(an):
   a. chain of amino acids
   b. organic molecule containing only carbon
   c. chain that stores energy
   d. complex lipid
   e. molecule that stores genetic information

7. One of the by-products of photosynthesis is:
   a. water
   b. energy released into the surrounding environment
   c. oxygen
   d. carbon dioxide
   e. energy contained in the water molecules

8. During the process of cellular respiration:
   a. solar energy trapped in photosynthesis is released
   b. carbon dioxide and water form sugars
   c. solar energy is transformed into chemical energy
   d. oxygen and carbon dioxide are produced
   e. sunlight is used to create energy
9. In primary production:
   a. oxygen utilized by animals is less than the oxygen produced by plants
   b. carbon dioxide is released into the water
   c. oxygen is utilized by plants
   d. organic matter is produced in excess of organic matter broken down by respiration
   e. proteins are manufactured by animals
10. The most important nutrients for plant growth in the ocean are:
    a. sodium and chloride
    b. nitrogen and oxygen
    c. carbon dioxide and oxygen
    d. oxygen and vitamins
    e. nitrogen and phosphorus
11. Which of the following is not true of a cell?
    a. it is the basic structural unit of life
    b. mitochondria are found in both plant and animal cells
    c. the cell membrane allows all substances to pass in out of the cell
    d. all organisms are made of one or more cells
    e. the membrane-bound structures with most cells are called organelles
12. Prokaryotes:
    a. are more organized and complex than eukaryotes
    b. include bacteria
    c. have many organelles in their cells
    d. all carry out photosynthesis
    e. have a nucleus in their cells
13. All of the following are organelles except:
    a. endoplasmic reticulum
    b. DNA
    c. nucleus
    d. mitochondria
    e. chloroplasts
14. Which of the following shows the correct level of organization in order of increasing complexity?
    a. molecule, cell, organelle, individual, community
    b. organelle, tissue, organ, community, population
    c. ecosystem, individual, organ, cell
    d. molecule, atom, cell, organ system, ecosystem
    e. atom, molecule, organ, population, ecosystem
15. A group of mussels of a particular type living together on a rocky beach is an example of a(an):
    a. population
    b. community
    c. individual
    d. ecosystem
    e. colony of individuals

16. The ecosystem best encompasses one of the following:
    a. all living organisms living in one area
    b. populations in one area but not the physical environment
    c. the community or communities but not the physical environment
    d. the community or communities and the physical environment
    e. populations and communities living in one area
17. Which of the following correctly links the type of organisms with the way they live?
    a. organisms part of the nekton swim
    b. organisms part of the benthos drift
    c. organisms part of the plankton live on the bottom
    d. organisms part of the nekton live on the bottom
    e. organisms part of the benthos swim
18. The cell membrane is said to be "selectively permeable" because it:
    a. allows only some substances to move through
    b. allows all substances to enter the cell
    c. allows all substances to leave the cell
    d. allows only the smallest molecules to enter the cell
    e. allows only water and salts to enter the cell
19. Marine organisms whose internal salt concentration varies with that of their environment are examples of:
    a. osmoregulators
    b. freshwater organisms
    c. ion-concentrators
    d. osmoconformers
    e. urea-concentrators
20. Typical marine fishes:
    a. tend to gain water by osmosis since their internal salt concentration is higher than that of seawater
    b. tend to lose water by osmosis since their internal salt concentration is lower than that of seawater
    c. do not drink seawater since they need to conserve as much water as possible
    d. produce a large volume of urine since they need to conserve as much water as possible
    e. drink seawater and as a result produce large amounts of urine
21. The term "ecotherms" is applied to those organisms:
    a. commonly known as "warm blooded"
    b. where the internal temperature is more or less kept constant
    c. where the internal temperature varies with that of the environment
    d. commonly known as "heat-producers"
    e. where the internal salt concentration as well as their temperature are kept constant
22. All of the following are examples of asexual reproduction except:
    a. fission
    b. fertilization
    c. plants sending out "runners"
    d. budding
    e. cell division

23. Male gametes (sperm) and female gametes (eggs):
    a. contain a diploid (2n) number of chromosomes
    b. are produced by mitosis
    c. fuse during fertilization
    d. are typically the largest cells in an organism
    e. are involved in producing identical clones of an organism
24. Which of the following shows the correct taxonomic level?
    a. kingdom, phylum, order, species, genus
    b. kingdom, phylum, family, genus, species
    c. kingdom, family, order, phylum, genus
    d. kingdom, order, phylum, genus, species
    e. order, family, phylum, genus, species
25. Which of the following are not correctly paired?
    a. Kingdom Plantae — sea lettuce
    b. Kingdom Fungi — mushrooms
    c. Kingdom Animalia — dolphins
    d. Kingdom Monera — sponges
    e. Kingdom Protista — single-celled plankton

CHAPTER 5
MARINE PROKARYOTES, PROTISTS, FUNGI, AND PLANTS

1. Prokaryotes are included in the kingdom:
   a. Animalia
   b. Fungi
   c. Plantae
   d. Monera
   e. Protista

2. Which of the following is not true of decay bacteria?
   a. break down waste products and dead organic matter
   b. carry out photosynthesis
   c. are heterotrophs
   d. are particularly abundant in bottom sediments
   e. ensure the recycling of essential nutrients

3. Bacteria that make their own organic compounds by obtaining energy from chemical compounds and not directly from light are known as:
   a. heterotrophic
   b. decay
   c. photosynthetic
   d. protists
   e. chemosynthetic

4. Cyanobacteria, or blue-green algae, are characterized by being:
   a. decomposers
   b. found only in the plankton
   c. having a glass-like skeleton
   d. protists
   e. photosynthetic

5. Stromatolites are:
   a. planktonic cyanobacteria
   b. organisms that cause red tides
   c. calcareous deposits deposited by cyanobacteria
   d. decay bacteria found in coral reefs
   e. heterotrophic bacteria that utilize other bacteria as a source of energy

6. Organisms having a shell made of silica (SiO_2):
   a. forams
   b. stromatolites
   c. cyanobacteria
   d. diatoms
   e. ciliates

7. Algae are:
   a. eukaryotic
   b. only unicellular
   c. all heterotrophic
   d. only multicellular
   e. have true leaves and roots

8. Diatoms are mostly:
   a. heterotrophs
   b. planktonic
   c. multicellular
   d. red in color
   e. prokaryotic
9. Reproduction in diatoms is:
   a. only asexual
   b. by budding
   c. asexual and sexual
   d. only sexual
   e. only during blooms
10. Red tides are caused mostly by:
    a. diatoms
    b. forams
    c. dinoflagellates
    d. protists
    e. radiolarians
11. Dinoflagellates that live in association with reef-building corals and other animals are known as:
    a. zooxanthellae
    b. zooplankton
    c. silicoflagellates
    d. bioluminescent dinoflagellates
    e. cryptomonads
12. The dominant group of planktonic primary producers in cold water:
    a. forams
    b. silicoflagellates
    c. dinoflagellates
    d. photosynthetic bacteria
    e. diatoms
13. Marine fungi:
    a. are mostly photosynthetic
    b. are part of lichens that live on rocky shores
    c. secrete calcareous skeletons
    d. produce red tides
    e. none of the above: there are no marine fungi
14. Which of the following does not apply to protozoans?
    a. multicellular
    b. their name derives from "first animals"
    c. some are heterotrophs
    d. members of the kingdom Protista
    e. some are autotrophs
15. Radiolarians are characterized by:
    a. being mostly planktonic
    b. having a calcareous skeleton
    c. being autotrophs
    d. having two flagella
    e. causing red tides

16. Which of the following are <u>not</u> protozoans?
    a. radiolarians
    b. forams
    c. dinoflagellates
    d. ciliates
    e. unicellular, planktonic organisms whose sediments form huge limestone deposits on land
17. Which of the following are <u>not</u> protists?
    a. dinoflagellates
    b. cyanobacteria
    c. diatoms
    d. forams
    e. ciliates
18. Seaweeds, or macrophytes, can be best differentiated from the other algae because seaweeds:
    a. are eukaryotic
    b. are photosynthetic
    c. have true roots
    d. are mostly multicellular
    e. have true leaves
19. The thallus of a seaweed refers to its:
    a. anchoring structure
    b. gas-filled bladders
    c. stem-like part of the body
    d. complete body
    e. leaf-like structures, or blades
20. Green algae are characterized by:
    a. being mostly unicellular
    b. being mostly marine
    c. having chlorophyll plus red pigments
    d. having true roots
    e. having pigments similar to land plants
21. Coralline green and red algae receive this name due to their ability to:
    a. emit light
    b. accumulate calcium carbonate
    c. be responsible for red tides
    d. live together with corals in coral reefs
    e. be parasites of other algae
22. The group of seaweeds with the largest number of species are the:
    a. green algae
    b. brown algae
    c. kelps
    d. red algae
    e. coralline algae
23. Reproduction in seaweeds can be very complex. It generally includes:
    a. only sexual reproduction
    b. only asexual reproduction
    c. both sexual and asexual reproduction
    d. only mitosis
    e. only meiosis

24. Marine flowering plants include all of the following except:
    a. mangroves
    b. kelps
    c. seagrasses
    d. cord grass
    e. surf grass
25. Marine flowering plants can be best differentiated from seaweeds by the fact that the marine flowering plants:
    a. have smaller flowers
    b. must be covered by water at all times
    c. must reproduce in the water
    d. can only live along rivers near the coast
    e. reproduce by seeds

CHAPTER 6
MARINE ANIMALS WITHOUT A BACKBONE

1. Animals, members of the kingdom Animalia are characterized by all of the following <u>except</u> one:
    a. prokaryotic and eukaryotic
    b. mostly multicellular
    c. some are autotrophs
    d. lack a backbone
    e. eukaryotic and unicellular

2. Which of the following type of cells and structures of a sponge does <u>not</u> match the function?
    a. collar cells — calcareous structures for support
    b. osculum — opening through which water leaves
    c. pore cells — opening through which water enters
    d. spongin — fibers for support
    e. gametes — reproduction

3. All sponges share one of these features:
    a. marine
    b. reproduce by asexual reproduction only
    c. relatively simple but sophisticated nervous system
    d. nematocysts
    e. multicellular

4. Sponges and all filter feeders use the following as a food source:
    a. plankton only
    b. all particulate matter suspended in water
    c. particular matter that deposits on the bottom
    d. dead plankton only
    e. vegetable matter in the water

5. A larva is best defined as:
    a. immature stage that is able to reproduce
    b. early colony of cells of freshwater sponges
    c. early stage of development of an organism, typically part of plankton
    d. sperm cell that lives free in the water
    e. egg that has been fertilized by more that one sperm

6. All cnidarians share all of these features <u>except</u> <u>one</u>:
    a. nematocysts
    b. multicellular
    c. radial symmetry
    d. complete digestive tract with two openings
    e. marine and freshwater

7. An example of an anthozoan:
    a. Portuguese man-of war
    b. colonial hydroid
    c. sea nettle jellyfish
    d. sea wasp
    e. reef corals

8. Most cnidarians are specialized as:
   a. filter feeders
   b. parasites
   c. carnivores
   d. plant-feeders
   e. feeders of organic matter on the bottom
9. Statocysts are structures use in:
   a. sensing balance
   b. capturing prey
   c. reproduction
   d. swimming movements
   e. digesting food
10. Comb jellies are:
    a. bilaterally symmetrical
    b. similar to a cnidarian polyp
    c. distinguished by eight bands of cilia
    d. colonial animals
    e. carnivores that use nematocysts to capture prey
11. In a bilaterally symmetrical animal, which of the following is not correctly paired?
    a. dorsal — upper surface
    b. anterior — head
    c. posterior — rear end
    d. ventral — brain
12. The development of bilateral symmetry in invertebrates has particularly influenced the evolution of a more complex:
    a. digestive system
    b. reproductive system
    c. skeleton
    d. mouth
    e. nervous system
13. Flatworms are characterized by having:
    a. radial symmetry
    b. a central nervous system
    c. tentacles used for filter feeding
    d. nematocysts
    e. a complete digestive tract
14. One group of parasites of fishes, seabirds, and other marine animals:
    a. flukes
    b. turbellarians
    c. comb jellies
    d. ribbon worms
    e. segmented worms
15. The most distinctive feature of ribbon worms:
    a. long proboscis
    b. segmented body
    c. absence of a digestive tract
    d. long bands of cilia used in locomotion
    e. radial symmetry

16. Which of the following is <u>not</u> correctly paired?
    a. phylum Ctenophora — comb jellies
    b. phylum Nematoda — roundworms
    c. phylum Nemertea — ribbon worms
    d. phylum Platyhelminthes — beard worms
    e. phylum Porifera — sponges
17. The trocophore is a:
    a. defensive structure
    b. larva
    c. planktonic cnidarian
    d. feeding structure
    e. filter-feeding worm
18. Deposit-feeding animals feed on:
    a. blood and living tissues
    b. particulate matter in the water
    c. plankton from the water that passively enters the digestive system
    d. live prey
    e. organic matter that settles on the bottom
19. Polychaete worms show:
    a. a body covered with a mantle
    b. segmentation
    c. radial symmetry
    d. incomplete digestive tract
    e. U-shaped gut
20. Beard worms are unique because they lack:
    a. symmetry
    b. a skin
    c. a digestive tract
    d. cells or tissues
    e. a reproductive system
21. Arrow worms feed on:
    a. organic matter that deposits on the bottom
    b. plant matter
    c. nutrients dissolved in the water
    d. live prey
    e. organic matter filtered from the water
22. The basic characteristics of lophophorates include all of the following <u>except</u>:
    a. U-shaped gut
    b. bilateral symmetry
    c. presence of nematocysts
    d. absence of segmentation
    e. presence of an anus
23. All molluscs:
    a. have a soft body often covered by a shell made of silica
    b. have a soft body covered by a mantle
    c. have an externally segmented body
    d. lack a larval stage
    e. lack a circulatory system

74

24. Which of the following are not correctly paired?
    a. class Gastropoda — mussels
    b. class Bivalvia — oysters
    c. class Polyplacophora — chitons
    d. class Cephalopoda — octopus
25. The radula and crystalline style of molluscs are part of the:
    a. reproductive system
    b. defensive mechanisms
    c. excretory system
    d. nervous system
    e. digestive system
26. Nudibranchs are members of which group of molluscs?
    a. cephalopods
    b. chitons
    c. bivalves
    d. gastropods
    e. tusk shells
27. One distinctive feature of arthropods:
    a. lack of a digestive system
    b. jointed legs
    c. gills in a mantle cavity
    d. proboscis used to capture prey
    e. lack of a brain
28. One of the following in not a crustacean:
    a. horseshoe crab
    b. copepods
    c. barnacles
    d. shrimps
    e. beach hoppers
29. One distinctive feature of all echinoderms:
    a. jointed legs
    b. gill slits
    c. endoskeleton
    d. water vascular system
    e. bilateral symmetry
30. Which of the following are not correctly paired?
    a. class Asteroidea — sea stars
    b. class Holothuroidea — sea cucumbers
    c. class Ophiuroidea — brittle stars
    d. class Echinoidea — feather stars

CHAPTER 7
MARINE FISHES

1. One of the following is <u>not</u> a characteristic of all chordates:
   a. gill slits
   b. backbone
   c. notochord
   d. dorsal nerve cord
   e. bilateral symmetry
2. The group of vertebrates containing the largest number of species:
   a. mammals
   b. amphibians
   c. birds
   d. fishes
   e. reptiles
3. An example of a jawless fish:
   a. ray
   b. shark
   c. hagfish
   d. whale shark
   e. skate
4. The whale shark feeds on:
   a. plankton
   b. large fishes
   c. small fishes
   d. organic matter from the bottom
   e. bottom-dwelling fishes and clams
5. The caudal fins of sharks are located on:
   a. the tail end
   b. dorsal surface close to the tail
   c. ventral surface close to the tail
   d. ventral surface close to the mouth
   e. dorsal surface close to the mouth
6. Demersal fishes:
   a. live on the surface of the water
   b. feed on plankton
   c. are parasites
   d. are part of the plankton
   e. live on the bottom
7. Rays and skates typically feed on:
   a. plankton
   b. seaweeds
   c. large fishes
   d. organic matter that accumulates on the bottom
   e. small animals that live on the bottom

8. One of the following characterizes bony fishes in general:
   a. upper lobe of tail is almost always longer than lower lobe
   b. scales are very small
   c. gill slits are exposed
   d. presence of an operculum
   e. mouth is ventral in position
9. One particular feature found in bony fishes but absent in cartilaginous fishes:
   a. scales
   b. gills
   c. swim bladder
   d. pectoral fin
   e. skeleton
10. When a particular color pattern allows animals like fishes to blend with their surroundings:
    a. cryptic coloration
    b. warning coloration
    c. defensive color
    d. countershading
    e. structural color
11. The shiny color of many fishes is the result of:
    a. countershading
    b. chromatophores
    c. disruptive coloration
    d. warning coloration
    e. algae that grow on the scales
12. In many sharks, extra buoyancy is provided by the:
    a. dorsal fin
    b. swim bladder
    c. liver
    d. mouth
    e. gills
13. The gill rakers are involved in which of the following?
    a. protecting gills
    b. filtering food in filter-feeding fishes
    c. extracting extra oxygen from the water
    d. providing extra buoyancy
    e. defense
14. Basking sharks feed on:
    a. plankton
    b. small fishes
    c. large fishes such as sharks
    d. marine mammals such as seals
    e. dead animals
15. Fishes with a small mouth located at the end of a long, thin "bill" are more likely to feed on:
    a. large seaweeds such as kelp
    b. larger fishes
    c. plankton that is filtered from the water
    d. very small animals
    e. other fish of the same species

16. Chemical digestion in fishes usually begins in the:
    a. mouth
    b. esophagus
    c. stomach
    d. liver
    e. intestine
17. In fishes, the function of the liver is to:
    a. absorb nutrients
    b. produce saliva
    c. aid in the digestion of plant material
    d. secrete hormones
    e. produce bile, which is used in the digestion of fats
18. The heart of all fishes has how many chambers?
    a. one
    b. two
    c. three
    d. four
19. Spiracles are involved in:
    a. filter feeding
    b. removing additional oxygen from the water
    c. increasing the surface area of the shark's intestine
    d. carrying additional blood to the heart
    e. allowing fishes like rays to take in water even when the mouth is buried in sediment
20. The function of arteries in fishes is to:
    a. carry oxygenated blood from the heart to the rest of the body
    b. circulate blood around the gills
    c. bring blood from the body to the heart
    d. collect deoxygenated blood from gills
    e. carry deoxygenated blood from the heart to the brain
21. Oxygen is carried in the blood of fishes by what protein?
    a. hemoglobin
    b. urea
    c. salts
    d. myoglobin
    e. chloride ions
22. The countercurrent system of flow is involved in:
    a. increasing blood flow into gills
    b. decreasing the time it takes for blood to flow through gills
    c. increasing the amount of oxygen that diffuses into the blood
    d. increasing the efficiency of the movement of gills
    e. increasing heart rate
23. The purpose of the lateral line in fishes:
    a. producing sound waves
    b. seeing particular colors
    c. detecting vibrations
    d. carrying blood along skin
    e. ingestion of food in rays

24. The nictitating membrane of sharks:
    a. produces sound
    b. detects chemicals in water
    c. detects vibrations in water
    d. is involved in digestion
    e. moves across the eye
25. Anadromous fishes migrate:
    a. up and down the water column
    b. from fresh water to reproduce at sea
    c. from polar regions to the tropics
    d. from the sea to reproduce in fresh water
    e. along the Equator to reproduce along the coast
26. An example of a catadromous fish:
    a. whale shark
    b. freshwater eel
    c. parrotfish
    d. Pacific salmon
    e. Atlantic salmon
27. One of the following is a synonym of spawning:
    a. copulation
    b. internal fertilization
    c. external fertilization
    d. mating
    e. courtship
28. The claspers are structures involved in:
    a. copulation
    b. osmoregulation
    c. courtship behavior
    d. detection of vibrations in water
    e. intake of oxygen by gills
29. Ovoviviparous fishes:
    a. release eggs, which are then fertilized in the water
    b. have embryos that take nutrients from the mother's reproductive tract
    c. release already fertilized but undeveloped eggs
    d. release sperm in packets
    e. retain fertilized eggs for development
30. Most marine fishes are:
    a. live-bearers
    b. ovoviviparous
    c. viviparous
    d. oviparous
    e. catadromous

1. Marine amphibians:
   a. do not exist at all
   b. are gill-breathers
   c. are fish-like
   d. include only tropical species
   e. are oviparous
2. All tetrapods are:
   a. endotherms
   b. inhabitants of land
   c. air-breathers
   d. live-bearers
   e. vertebrates except groups such as sea squirts
3. All reptiles are:
   a. dependent on water for reproduction
   b. meat-eaters
   c. ovoviviparous
   d. ectotherms
   e. gill-breathers
4. One of these is not a characteristic of sea turtles:
   a. oviparous
   b. leave the water to reproduce
   c. have a shell that is free from the backbone
   d. are tetrapods
   e. are "cold-blooded"
5. Sea snakes feed mostly on:
   a. large fishes
   b. seaweeds and other marine plants
   c. polyps of live coral
   d. worms and other small, bottom invertebrates
   e. small fishes
6. Penguins:
   a. live on polar regions of the Northern and Southern Hemispheres
   b. can be found as far as the Equator
   c. are ectotherms
   d. time their reproduction so that eggs hatch during the winter
   e. are able to fly when disturbed
7. Seals, sea lions, and the walrus are classified as belonging to the order:
   a. Carnivora
   b. Sirenia
   c. Pinnipedia
   d. Cetacea

8. Sea lions can be readily distinguished from the seals because in contrast to seals they have:
   a. a short neck
   b. uses the posterior flippers in swimming
   c. anterior flippers cannot be rotated backward
   d. posterior flippers cannot be rotated backward
   e. external ears
9. The walrus feeds mostly on:
   a. clams
   b. squid
   c. salmon and other fish
   d. kelp and other large seaweeds
   e. dead animals
10. We can tell that cetaceans are mammals because they:
    a. have hair
    b. are cold-blooded
    c. are ovoviviparous
    d. must reproduce in the water
    e. migrate
11. Only one of these is a toothed whale:
    a. dolphin
    b. right
    c. gray
    d. fin
    e. blue
12. An example of a baleen whale:
    a. common porpoise
    b. killer
    c. sperm
    d. blue
    e. common porpoise
13. Blubber is found in all of these marine mammals except:
    a. killer whales
    b. seals
    c. sea otters
    d. sea lions
    e. manatees (sea cows)
14. The largest of all of the whales is the blue; the second largest:
    a. right
    b. fin
    c. killer
    d. gray
    e. minke
15. The gray whale feed mostly on:
    a. small plankton
    b. small fishes
    c. squid
    d. largest plankton
    e. bottom crustaceans

16. Baleen plates are:
    a. rigid and having small hairs on one side only
    b. soft and having hairs all around their surface
    c. rigid and having hairs all around their surface
    d. rigid without any hairs
    e. soft without any hairs
17. Baleen whales lack:
    a. flukes
    b. teeth
    c. a dorsal fin
    d. a blowhole
    e. ear openings
18. An example of a whale known as a rorqual:
    a. killer
    b. gray
    c. common porpoise
    d. blue
    e. sperm
19. Ambergris, used in the manufacture of perfumes, comes from what part of whales?
    a. sperm oil
    b. baleen
    c. skin
    d. melon
    e. undigested food
20. Dolphins and other whales are adapted for deep diving by:
    a. closing their ear openings
    b. emitting sound to clear their ears
    c. taking as much air as possible
    d. increasing blood circulation to the skin
    e. collapsing their lungs
21. One of the following is not an adaptation for deep diving in cetaceans:
    a. having more red blood cells to store more oxygen
    b. having more hemoglobin to store more oxygen
    c. slowing down of heart rate
    d. blood flow is shifted from the brain to the extremities
    e. having a lot of myoglobin in muscles to store more oxygen
22. Echolocation is a sense that relies on:
    a. vibrations
    b. sound
    c. smell
    d. vision
    e. electromagnetic waves
23. Echolocation is present in:
    a. all baleen whales
    b. some baleen whales
    c. all toothed whales
    d. some toothed whales
    e. only in dolphins and porpoises

24. The spermaceti organ of sperm whales is thought to regulate buoyancy and:
    a. storage of food
    b. production of sound
    c. assist in oxygen storage
    d. collect undigested food
    e. focus and direct sound waves
25. Breaching refers to whales:
    a. jumping above the surface
    b. getting stranded on shore
    c. singing
    d. emitting sound for navigation
    e. diving deep to feed
26. The humpback and other baleen whales migrate every year:
    a. to feed in Antarctica during winter
    b. to reproduce in Antarctica during summer
    c. to reproduce in the tropics during winter
    d. to feed in the tropics during winter
    e. to feed in the tropics during summer
27. In order to reduce drag, the penis of cetaceans is:
    a. small
    b. located just before the tail
    c. located just before the head
    d. internal until just before copulation
    e. absent
28. Delayed implantation of the embryo allows pinnipeds to:
    a. nurse a pup while pregnant
    b. time birth with arrival to breeding area
    c. delay courtship for a year
    d. establish harems
    e. ovulate after copulation
29. The migrating gray whale breeds:
    a. every six months
    b. every year
    c. every other year
    d. every two years
    e. every four years
30. One of the following alternatives does not apply to the typical cetacean calf:
    a. born tail first
    b. establishes a long and strong bond with its mother
    c. feeds on very rich milk that is squirted directly into its mouth
    d. is born with a developed blubber
    e. must swim to the surface immediately after birth

CHAPTER 9
AN INTRODUCTION TO ECOLOGY

1. All of the following are examples of abiotic factors <u>except</u> <u>one</u>:
   a. salinity
   b. predation
   c. substrate
   d. temperature
   e. light
2. An example of a community is:
   a. one giant kelp plant
   b. a kelp plant forest plus all physical factors affecting it
   c. all physical factors affecting a kelp forest
   d. a kelp forest plus all organisms living in it
   e. several kelp plants living in one particular area
3. A population may grow until its growth is slowed or stopped as a result of:
   a. predation
   b. lack of nutrients
   c. reduction in living space
   d. reduction in light
   e. all of the above
4. The type of interaction that results when a resource is in short supply and one organism uses the resource at the expense of the other is called:
   a. population explosion
   b. predation
   c. resource partitioning
   d. self-regulation
   e. competition
5. Competitive exclusion can be best defined as:
   a. when one species overcompetes and eliminates another
   b. the creation of a separate ecological niche by a new species
   c. the division of resources
   d. when one species shares limiting resources with another
   e. when competition results in the elimination of particular limiting resources
6. The ecological niche of a species is best defined as its:
   a. habitat
   b. habitat plus the most important physical factors affecting it
   c. role in the community
   d. mode of reproduction and food habits
   e. behavior in relation to other species in the community
7. Predation can be best defined as:
   a. a plant taking in nutrients
   b. an animal eating another animal
   c. an animal eating a plant
   d. an animal eating any other organism
   e. a plant carrying out photosynthesis

8. One of these is an example of coevolution:
   a. a seaweed evolving better ways to capture sunlight energy
   b. a seaweed evolving a mechanism allowing it to take in a particular nutrient
   c. a limpet getting adapted to live along coasts exposed to heavier wave action
   d. a limpet getting evolving a behavior that allows it to escape from a sea star predator
   e. a sea star becoming adapted to move higher up along rocky shores during low tides
9. The relationship between zooxanthellae and reef corals is an example of:
   a. mutualism
   b. predation
   c. commensalism
   d. parasitism
   e. cleaning symbiosis
10. Cleaning symbiosis is an example of symbiosis because the partners involved in the association:
    a. are not harmed
    b. are both harmed if we closely study their association
    c. both have coevolved into a close association
    d. one is harmed while the other is not
    e. one species benefits while the other is unaffected
11. The following is a synonym of autotrophs:
    a. consumer
    b. primary producer
    c. heterotroph
    d. animal
    e. predator
12. The difference between food webs and food chains is that food webs:
    a. consist of only one trophic level
    b. include primary producers as well as consumers
    c. do not take into account predators
    d. only outline feeding relationships among consumers
    e. are more complex
13. Consumers that feed directly on the producers are called:
    a. top predators
    b. secondary consumers
    c. carnivores
    d. primary consumers
    e. parasites
14. An example of a tertiary consumer:
    a. a seaweed
    b. a grazer
    c. a carnivore
    d. an autotroph
    e. a herbivore
15. On the average, what percentage of energy in a particular trophic level is passed on to the next trophic level?
    a. 1%
    b. 2%
    c. 5%
    d. 10%
    e. 15%

16. The pyramid of numbers shows the:
    a. transfer of energy between each trophic level
    b. energy in each trophic level
    c. biomass in each trophic level
    d. number of species in each trophic level
    e. number of individuals in each trophic level
17. The detritus in the water includes:
    a. dead organic matter
    b. waste products dissolved in water
    c. all of the plankton
    d. smallest plankton-feeding fishes
    e. smallest algae
18. A fundamental role of decomposers:
    a. releasing nutrients for autotrophs
    b. causing diseases
    c. providing food for carnivores
    d. releasing oxygen
    e. providing energy for autotrophs
19. Primary production is measured using the following units:
    a. gm carbon/depth
    b. gm carbon/time
    c. volume of water/depth/time
    d. gm carbon/area/time
    e. volume oxygen/time
20. In the dark-light bottle experiment, one of the following is measured in the dark bottle:
    a. photosynthesis
    b. respiration
    c. decomposition
    d. photosynthesis plus respiration
    e. chlorophyll concentration
21. The amount of chlorophyll in the water is a direct estimate of:
    a. primary production
    b. respiration
    c. standing stock of phytoplankton
    d. oxygen utilization
    e. release of nutrients
22. In the carbon cycle, plants play a fundamental role by:
    a. increasing the amount of dissolved carbon dioxide as a result of decomposition
    b. decreasing the amount of dissolved carbon dioxide as a result of respiration
    c. increasing the amount of dissolved carbon dioxide as a result of photosynthesis
    d. decreasing the amount of detritus
    e. both increasing the amount of dissolved carbon dioxide as a result of respiration and decreasing it as a result of photosynthesis
23. Nitrogen fixation is performed at sea by:
    a. seaweeds
    b. cyanobacteria (blue-green algae)
    c. phytoplankton
    d. zooplankton
    e. all of the above

24. Sessile organisms are part of the:
    a. benthos
    b. nekton
    c. plankton
    d. pelagic type of organisms
    e. zooplankton only
25. The subtidal zone is the area:
    a. between low and high tide
    b. beyond the continental shelf
    c. between the intertidal zone and the continental shelf
    d. where pelagic organisms live
    e. above the highest tide

CHAPTER 10
BETWEEN THE TIDES

1. The lower limit of the intertidal zone is the:
   a. average high tide
   b. average middle tide
   c. lowest tide
   d. lowest edge of the rocky substrate
   e. none of the above: it varies according to type of substrate
2. The particular characteristic most widely used in classifying intertidal communities:
   a. type of tides
   b. relative exposure to air
   c. type of substrate
   d. type of seaweeds
   e. relative immersion by water
3. Regarding the origin of rocky coasts, it is known that this type of shore is present along:
   a. geologically young coasts
   b. coasts with high accumulation of sediments
   c. coasts along the mouth of large rivers
   d. geologically old coasts being covered by sediments
   e. coasts being affected by ice sheets
4. The sessile epifauna consists of:
   a. attached seaweeds
   b. pelagic organisms
   c. burrowing animals
   d. animals that crawl over bottom
   e. attached animals
5. Many rocky-shore animals cope with desiccation by:
   a. moving up the intertidal
   b. crowding in areas that are always moist
   c. opening their shells
   d. expanding or elongating their soft bodies
   e. moving out of tide pools
6. Which type of shell would be most suited to live on a rocky shore that is exposed at low tide?
   a. black, smooth
   b. black, ridged
   c. white, smooth
   d. white, ridged
   e. no shell at all
7. Most sessile animals living on rocky shores are:
   a. deposit feeders
   b. carnivores
   c. detritus feeders
   d. filter feeders
   e. grazers

8. One of these organisms is expected to be relatively rare on a rocky shore:
   a. filter feeder
   b. carnivore
   c. primary producer
   d. grazer
   e. deposit feeder
9. If a rocky shore highly exposed to wave action is compared to a similar rocky shore that is a lot less exposed to wave action, we should expect that barnacles living on the more exposed shore show a:
   a. wider vertical distribution
   b. narrower tolerance to salinity
   c. narrower tolerance to temperature
   d. narrower vertical distribution
   e. higher resistance to predators
10. The reason why rocky shores have few deposit feeders:
    a. abundant detritus
    b. high wave action
    c. numerous carnivores
    d. no filter feeders
    e. high salinity
11. Refraction causes waves to:
    a. slow down
    b. approach the shore at an angle
    c. become more parallel to the shore
    d. break
    e. speed up
12. One of these is more important than the others as a limiting resource in intertidal communities:
    a. space
    b. food
    c. nutrients
    d. light
    e. salinity
13. Vertical zonation on rocky shores is mostly the result of differences in tolerance to:
    a. wave action
    b. exposure
    c. predation
    d. light
    e. salinity
14. The upper limit of rocky intertidal communities is typically determined by:
    a. biological factors only
    b. physical factors only
    c. biological and physical factors
    d. neither physical or biological factors
15. One organism typical of the upper intertidal on rocky shores:
    a. mussels
    b. barnacles
    c. sponges
    d. sea anemones
    e. periwinkles

16. The middle intertidal is characterized by:
    a. constant wetting by splash and spray
    b. long exposure to air
    c. steady immersion
    d. exposure and immersion on a regular basis
    e. splashing during high tide and complete exposure at low tide
17. An example of a keystone predator on rocky shores:
    a. periwinkles
    b. limpets
    c. sea stars
    d. hermit crabs
    e. sponges
18. Predation by sea stars on rocky shores ultimately results in:
    a. fewer species
    b. less wave action
    c. decrease in the number of seaweeds
    d. increase in the number of mussels
    e. more species
19. Ecological succession ultimately results in:
    a. a climax community
    b. an upper-limit stage
    c. competitive exclusion
    d. keystone predation
    e. vertical zonation
20. In addition to space, another factor that is typically limiting in the lower intertidal along rocky shores:
    a. salinity
    b. grazing
    c. temperature
    d. type of substrate
    e. nutrients
21. One of these organisms is typically a very rare component of soft-bottom intertidal communities:
    a. burrowing organisms
    b. detritus feeders
    c. seaweeds
    d. infauna
    e. deposit feeders
22. Most animals living on sandy beaches are included among the:
    a. infauna
    b. deposit feeders
    c. epifauna
    d. producers
    e. grazers

23. Fine sediments are characteristic of:
    a. shores exposed to wave action
    b. rocky shores
    c. areas with wide temperature fluctuations
    d. calm, less exposed shores
    e. areas that experience considerable water flow
24. In terms of oxygen, the interstitial water in muddy bottoms:
    a. has plenty of it since temperature is much higher than in the water column
    b. accumulates it as a result of photosynthesis by inhabitants of the sediment
    c. recirculates very frequently so it is high
    d. is deficient in it
    e. is deficient in it but only during the day
25. The main source of food in muddy-bottom intertidal communities:
    a. seaweeds
    b. detritus
    c. plankton
    d. large pray
    e. epifauna

CHAPTER 11
ESTUARIES: WHERE RIVERS MEET THE SEA

1. Coastal plain estuaries were formed when:
   a. sand bars formed along the coast as the result of an accumulation of sediment
   b. the ocean invaded lowlands and river mouths
   c. retreating glaciers cut a valley along the coast
   d. sea level fell during glaciation
   e. land subsided along the coast

2. Good examples of a bar-built estuaries are found here:
   a. coast of Norway
   b. Pacific coast of the United States
   c. Atlantic coast of the United States
   d. Chesapeake Bay
   e. St. Lawrence River

3. Fjords are formed as a result of the:
   a. subsidence of land
   b. lowering of sea level
   c. formation of sand bars and barrier islands
   d. the coast is cut by a river
   e. raising of sea level

4. In an estuary, salinity of the water increases as:
   a. one moves inland
   b. depth decreases
   c. evaporation decreases
   d. freshwater flow from a river increases
   e. depth increases

5. The salt wedge of an estuary:
   a. moves inland as tide moves in
   b. is found in shallower water as one moves inland
   c. decreases the average salinity of the estuary
   d. decreases the distribution of marine organisms along the bottom of the estuary
   e. spreads further into the estuary as the flow of freshwater increases

6. Tidal bores in estuaries result from the effect of:
   a. freshwater moving from rivers
   b. the Coriolis effect
   c. high tides moving in
   d. salt wedge moving toward the surface
   e. differences in water temperature as one moves inland

7. The most common type of substrate in estuaries:
   a. mud
   b. rock
   c. coarse sand
   d. fine sand
   e. none of the above: it depends on the salinity

8. The amount of hydrogen sulfide in the sediment increases as the following factors increase <u>except</u> <u>one</u>:
   a. oxygen
   b. space between sediment particles
   c. size of sediment particles
   d. amount of organic matter
   e. amount of detritus
9. Euryhaline species:
   a. are less common in estuaries than stenohaline species
   b. need less oxygen to survive
   c. tolerate only a narrow range of salinities
   d. can survive changes in salinity
   e. only tolerate small temperature changes
10. Osmoconformers survive changes in salinity by:
    a. maintaining the salinity of their body fluids constant
    b. moving up and down the water column in order to spend most of the day in the salt wedge
    c. pumping water in as salinity decreases
    d. allowing the salinity of their body fluids to vary with that of the surrounding water
    e. increasing the amounts of salts in their body fluids no matter what the salinity of the surrounding water is
11. Salmon, which migrate between the sea and rivers, are an example of:
    a. osmoconformers
    b. stenohaline species
    c. catadromous species
    d. perfect osmoconformers
    e. osmoregulators
12. The most important difference between muddy intertidal shores and the mud flats of estuaries:
    a. type of substrate
    b. variation in salinity
    c. amount of light
    d. exposure to wave action
    e. size of sediment particles
13. An example of a primary producer on mud flats:
    a. benthic diatoms
    b. phytoplankton
    c. kelp
    d. surf grass
    e. mud snails
14. An example of a deposit feeder on mud flats:
    a. mud snails
    b. birds that feed on worms
    c. clams
    d. sulfur bacteria
    e. worms that feed on other worms

15. The most abundant type of mud-flat organisms:
    a. carnivores
    b. epifauna
    c. seaweeds
    d. infauna
    e. filter feeders
16. Succulents are plants that:
    a. excrete salts by way of salt glands
    b. lose water and salts
    c. accumulate water in their tissues
    d. take in salts to compensate for the loss of water
    e. do not have any roots to minimize water loss
17. The infauna of mud flats feeds mostly on:
    a. epifauna
    b. sulfur bacteria
    c. filter feeders
    d. plankton
    e. detritus
18. Blood rich in hemoglobin is an adaptation to:
    a. fluctuating salinities
    b. wide variations in temperature
    c. soft sediments
    d. feeding in detritus
    e. low oxygen concentrations
19. Zonation in an estuary is made evident by:
    a. large number of worms in the mud
    b. presence of different species along different horizontal levels in relation to tides
    c. tide pools along the mud flats
    d. absence of life in black sediments
    e. high concentration of plants in salt marshes
20. The zonation of plants in salt marshes is determined mostly by:
    a. temperature fluctuations
    b. geographical location
    c. height of the tide
    d. amount of oxygen in sediments
    e. detritus in the water
21. The food web in salt-marsh communities is characterized by high primary production. Most of this production is made available to other communities in the form of:
    a. plant tissue eaten by grazers
    b. plankton eaten by filter feeders
    c. detritus
    d. plants eaten by herbivores
    e. plants eaten by zooplankton
22. The geographical distribution of mangrove forests is mostly determined by:
    a. salinity
    b. type of sediment
    c. temperature
    d. wave action
    e. height of tide

23. Mangroves belong to one of the following groups:
    a. green algae
    b. brown algae
    c. seagrasses
    d. flowering plants
    e. kelps
24. Mangrove forests are considered a stage in the ecological succession between marine and terrestrial communities due to the fact that they:
    a. accumulate sediment in their roots
    b. produce large amounts of detritus
    c. serve as a nesting place for birds
    d. maintain a large concentration of nutrients
    e. live mostly above water
25. Outwelling in estuaries is most important since it:
    a. maintains high primary production
    b. provides living space to many species
    c. releases much oxygen
    d. provides food and nutrients to other communities
    e. allows plants to survive despite wide fluctuations in salinity

CHAPTER 12
LIFE ON THE CONTINENTAL SHELF

1. The part of the continental shelf that is never exposed at low tide is called the:
   a. littoral zone
   b. subtidal zone
   c. intertidal zone
   d. pelagic zone
   e. abyssal zone

2. The concentration of nutrients in the waters over the continental shelf is typically:
   a. higher than in the open ocean
   b. lower than in the open ocean
   c. about the same
   d. no generalizations can be made: the amount of nutrients depends on the type of substrate
   e. no generalizations can be made: the amount of nutrients depends on having or not having kelp

3. One of the following statements best describes the temperature and salinity of the deep water over the continental shelf:
   a. it is typically very different from that of the surface as a result of light affecting only the surface
   b. it is usually about the same along the entire water column as a result of the type of sediment
   c. it is usually about the same along the entire water column as a result of currents and wave action
   d. it is typically very different from that of the surface as a result of differences in nutrients
   e. it is typically very different from that of the surface as a result of the higher density of surface water

4. Most of the sediment over the continental shelf consists of:
   a. siliceous ooze
   b. calcareous ooze
   c. lithogenous
   d. biogenous
   e. a mixture of silicious and calcareous ooze

5. What type of animal is typically absent in soft-bottom subtidal communities?
   a. epifauna
   b. benthic
   c. infauna
   d. sessile
   e. deposit feeders

6. The distribution of the infauna of soft-bottom subtidal communities is often closely related to:
   a. temperature
   b. particle size of sediment
   c. salinity
   d. distribution of seaweeds
   e. light

7. The pattern of spatial distribution most often seen in soft-bottom subtidal communities:
   a. regular
   b. irregular
   c. random
   d. clumped
   e. patchy

8. Dredges are particularly useful in sampling what type of bottom in the subtidal zone?
   a. rocky
   b. soft
   c. muddy
   d. sandy
   e. covered with ooze
9. Settlement and metamorphosis in the planktonic larvae of many subtidal animals is determined or influenced by:
   a. biological factors such as presence of adults
   b. physical factors such as the type of bottom
   c. both biological and physical factors
   d. none of the above: larvae settle by chance
10. The most important food source in unvegetated soft-bottom subtidal communities:
    a. plankton
    b. drift seaweeds
    c. nekton
    d. benthic prey
    e. detritus
11. The meiofauna is the name given to those animals that live:
    a. on the surface of seagrass leaves
    b. inside worm tubes
    c. on kelp holdfasts
    d. between particles of sediment
    e. crawling on the bottom
12. The higher the water turbulence such as wave action, the higher the relative number of:
    a. planktonic species
    b. deposit feeders
    c. nektonic species
    d. filter feeders
    e. primary producers
13. As turbulence decreases:
    a. the amount of oxygen in the sediment decreases
    b. the amount of detritus in the sediment decreases
    c. the size of sediment particles increases
    d. the relative number of suspension feeders increases
    e. the relative number of seaweed species increases
14. One example of a filter feeder inhabiting soft bottoms in the subtidal region:
    a. brittle stars
    b. shrimps
    c. snails such as whelks
    d. sand dollars
    e. clams
15. Most species of seagrasses live:
    a. on rocky bottoms
    b. in the Arctic and Antarctic
    c. in temperate regions
    d. on kelp forests
    e. in tropical and subtropical regions

16. Most of the biomass produced by seagrasses find their way into the food chain by way of:
    a. small herbivores that eat the plants
    b. detritus
    c. epiphytes that live on the surface of leaves and also feed on the plants
    d. plankton that thrive on nutrients released by the plants
    e. large herbivores such as manatees and sea turtles that feed on the plants

17. Typically, the dominant inhabitants of rocky subtidal bottoms in shallow water are:
    a. limpets
    b. sea urchins
    c. seaweeds
    d. seagrasses
    e. sessile worms

18. One of the following will be relatively uncommon components of rocky subtidal communities:
    a. producers
    b. grazers
    c. predators
    d. infauna
    e. epifauna

19. By definition, kelp forests develop when:
    a. kelp fronds float on the surface
    b. the kelp is large enough to rise above the bottom
    c. the kelp lives in warm water
    d. kelp fronds have leaves
    e. the kelp holdfast is large enough to be called a true root system

20. The life cycle of the giant kelp involves:
    a. one growth form
    b. two growth forms
    c. two growth forms, both very large
    d. two or three growth forms, depending on temperature
    e. one growth form, which can be large or small depending on temperature

21. Kelps are characteristic of:
    a. soft bottoms
    b. Arctic and Antarctic coasts
    c. hard bottoms in the tropics
    d. soft bottoms but only in the tropics
    e. temperate regions

22. The distribution of kelps is expected to be the widest on coasts along the:
    a. eastern side of oceans
    b. western side of oceans
    c. Southern Hemisphere
    d. Northern Hemisphere
    e. Equator

23. The distribution of kelp species along a particular coast is known to be affected by all of the following factors except one:
    a. light
    b. wave action
    c. carnivorous fishes
    d. depth
    e. type of grazers

24. Sea otters are known to affect the development of giant kelp forests by:
   a. helping in the dispersion of spores
   b. removing competing seaweeds
   c. feeding on carnivorous fishes
   d. feeding on grazing sea urchins
   e. releasing nutrients present in feces and urine
25. Kelp communities are severely disturbed by all of the following except:
   a. grazing sea urchins
   b. grazing fishes
   c. pollution
   d. warm currents
   e. El Niño

CHAPTER 13
CORAL REEFS

1. Reef-building corals are cnidarians that are characterized by:
   a. having both a polyp and medusa stage
   b. lacking nematocysts
   c. having mostly a medusa stage
   d. lacking a mouth
   e. having only a polyp stage
2. Ahermatypic corals are those that:
   a. only live in tropical waters
   b. have zooxanthellae
   c. are carnivores
   d. are non-reef builders
   e. always have a soft skeleton
3. "Planula" is the name given to:
   a. the coral polyp
   b. zooxanthellae
   c. corals that do not build reefs
   d. coral larvae
   e. the coral skeleton
4. Zooxanthellae are essential to reef-building corals because they:
   a. provide the coral with carbon dioxide
   b. filter out harmful solar radiation
   c. provide the coral with protection from predators
   d. release mucus
   e. help in the deposition of the skeleton
5. The mesenterial filaments of corals are important because they:
   a. secrete digestive enzymes
   b. help deposit the skeleton
   c. digest zooxanthellae
   d. produce mucus
   e. perform photosynthesis
6. Sources of food and other essential nutrients for corals include all of the following except:
   a. nutrients released by zooxanthellae
   b. calcium carbonate from shells
   c. dissolved organic matter (DOM) from the water
   d. zooplankton captured by the tentacles
   e. capture of food using mesenterial filaments
7. The most important organisms that help form coral reefs, other than reef-building corals, are:
   a. sponges
   b. molluscs
   c. bryozoans
   d. coralline algae
   e. forams

8. Practically all of the sediment that accumulates in a coral reef is of what type?
   a. hydrogenous
   b. foraminiferan ooze
   c. biogenous
   d. lithogenous
   e. siliceous ooze

9. Reef-building corals grow only in shallow water because:
   a. salinity varies less in shallow water
   b. zooxanthellae need light for photosynthesis
   c. calcium carbonate is only available in shallow water
   d. nutrients concentrate in shallow water
   e. shallow water contains more dissolved organic matter (DOM)

10. The expulsion of zooxanthellae due to unfavorable conditions is called:
    a. exflagellation
    b. exudation
    c. bleaching
    d. decalcification
    e. denudation

11. Eutrophication is very detrimental to the development of coral since it increases:
    a. the amount of nutrients in the water, hence increasing stimulating the overgrowth of algae
    b. the temperature of the water, which kills the corals
    c. the temperature of the water, which kills the zooxanthellae
    d. the salinity of the water, which kills the corals
    e. the amount of pollutants in the water

12. The most common type of coral reefs around the world:
    a. barrier
    b. atolls
    c. coral knolls
    d. oyster reefs
    e. fringing

13. In a typical fringing reef, most of the live coral is found on the:
    a. reef flat
    b. fore-reef
    c. reef crest
    d. reef slope
    e. coral knolls

14. Fringing and barrier reefs develop:
    a. in waters along estuaries
    b. in the open ocean far from land
    c. along a coast
    d. around islands in temperate regions
    e. near atolls

15. Generally, one important distinction between barrier and fringing reefs is that barrier reefs:
    a. develop from atolls
    b. develop farther away from land
    c. are found only in the Pacific
    d. are found only in the Caribbean
    e. do not have a reef flat

16. Spur-and-groove formations, or buttresses, appear to be the result of:
    a. fish grazing
    b. the death of coralline algae
    c. accumulation of sand
    d. the death of coral after a series of very low tides
    e. wind and waves
17. Most atolls are found in the:
    a. Indo-west Pacific region
    b. Caribbean
    c. eastern Pacific along Central America
    d. the eastern Atlantic
    e. western Pacific along the Australian coast
18. Atolls actually start as a:
    a. fringing reef
    b. barrier reef
    c. semicircular or half-moon shaped atoll
    d. coral knoll
    e. reef flat
19. Aside from zooxanthellae, what is the other important primary producer in a coral reef?
    a. turf algae
    b. benthic diatoms
    c. kelps
    d. coralline algae
    e. cyanobacteria (blue-green algae)
20. Primary production is very high in coral reefs but low in surrounding waters. One reason for this is that:
    a. coralline algae and other algae are very abundant
    b. there is abundant carbon dioxide in coral reefs
    c. nutrients are efficiently recycled
    d. zooxanthellae increase the amount of dissolved oxygen in the water
    e. turf algae release nutrients
21. Reef corals compete with soft corals for space. One competitive advantage of soft corals is their:
    a. color
    b. toxic chemicals
    c. special stinging cells
    d. ability to destroy zooxanthellae of corals
    e. ability to dissolve the skeleton of corals
22. The lottery hypothesis states that:
    a. species tend to avoid competition
    b. each species has its own ecological niche but it is modified to avoid direct competition
    c. corals overcompete other organisms as long as they keep their zooxanthellae
    d. the outcome of competition is based mostly on chance
    e. species actually chose when to compete and when to move elsewhere
23. The sweeper tentacles of corals contain:
    a. zooxanthellae
    b. nematocysts
    c. specialized spicules
    d. bad-tasting chemicals
    e. harmful enzymes

24. Obligate symbionts are those organisms that:
    a. have a casual relationship with a host
    b. harm the host
    c. are found only in association with another species
    d. are neither beneficial nor harmful to their host
    e. benefit the host but derive no benefit from it
25. Giant clams are very large in size because of their ability to:
    a. utilize dissolved organic matter from the water
    b. filter a large volume of water
    c. be a deposit as well as a suspension feeder
    d. be parasites when young
    e. have zooxanthellae

CHAPTER 14
LIFE NEAR THE SURFACE

1. The epipelagic is divided into two components: the oceanic waters and the:
   a. photic zone
   b. neritic zone
   c. pelagic realm
   d. upper photic zone
   e. subtidal zone

2. Most of the primary production carried out in the open ocean is performed by:
   a. seaweeds
   b. kelps
   c. phytoplankton
   d. seagrasses
   e. zooxanthellae

3. Nanoplankton consists mostly of very small:
   a. phytoplankton
   b. copepods
   c. jellyfishes
   d. forms
   e. fish larvae

4. The net phytoplankton consists mostly of:
   a. copepods
   b. diatoms and dinoflagellates
   c. nanoplankton
   d. cyanobacteria (blue-green algae)
   e. nanoplankton and diatoms

5. Most zooplankton feed on:
   a. strictly phytoplankton
   b. strictly zooplankton
   c. mostly nanoplankton
   d. mostly zooplankton
   e. mostly nanoplankton and phytoplankton

6. The most abundant group in the zooplankton:
   a. larvaceans
   b. krill
   c. fish larvae
   d. nanoplankton
   e. copepods

7. Krill are more closely related to:
   a. sea urchins
   b. crabs
   c. brittle stars
   d. mussels
   e. fishes

8. Larvaceans are:
   a. planktonic chordates
   b. fish larvae
   c. sea urchin larvae
   d. deep-water crustaceans
   e. primitive fishes
9. One of these groups builds a mucus "house":
   a. copepods
   b. arrow worms
   c. larvaceans
   d. planktonic snails such as pteropods
   e. snail larvae
10. Only one of these is part of the meroplankton:
    a. copepods
    b. arrow worms
    c. larvaceans
    d. planktonic snails such as pteropods
    e. snail larvae
11. Arrow worms are:
    a. detritus feeders
    b. carnivores
    c. phytoplankton feeders
    d. parasites
    e. members of the nanoplankton
12. Most nekton feed on:
    a. zooplankton
    b. phytoplankton
    c. plankton and nekton
    d. other nekton
    e. phytoplankton and zooplankton
13. One of the following is an adaptation to the planktonic way of life except one:
    a. spines
    b. small size
    c. decrease in drag
    d. substitution of heavy ions by light ones
    e. gas-filled bladders
14. The storage of lipids within the body is an adaptation in plankton since lipids:
    a. make cells heavier
    b. increase body density
    c. contain air pockets so they help in buoyancy
    d. contain a larger amount of energy
    e. are less dense than water
15. The neuston consist of animals that:
    a. swim against currents
    b. sink to the bottom portion of the water column
    c. are top carnivores in the pelagic realm
    d. spend their entire lives in the plankton
    e. float on the surface

16. Countershading is a form of:
    a. shading with bioluminescence
    b. warning coloration
    c. structural coloration
    d. protective coloration
    e. cryptic coloration
17. The rete mirabile found in some fishes is involved in:
    a. increasing speed
    b. decreasing buoyancy
    c. digesting food
    d. increasing buoyancy
    e. conserving body heat
18. Zooplankton that migrates vertically:
    a. hibernate at night and feed during the day
    b. feed at the surface during the day, and migrate below the photic zone at night
    c. feed in the photic zone during the day, and migrate to the surface at night
    d. stay below the photic zone during the day, and feed at the surface at night
    e. migrate up and down but always stay below the photic zone
19. Most animals in the epipelagic are omnivores. This means that they eat:
    a. plants and animals
    b. part of the neuston
    c. zooplankton
    d. detritus
    e. phytoplankton
20. What is the relationship between dissolved organic matter (DOM) and bacteria in the epipelagic?
    a. bacteria feed on the DOM, making it available to other animals in the food chain that feed on bacteria
    b. bacteria supply most of the DOM
    c. bacteria feed on DOM and thus it is unavailable to other animals
    d. bacteria cannot utilize DOM and thus feed on detritus, depleting it through most of the epipelagic
    e. bacteria cannot utilize DOM, making it available to animals
21. The most common limiting nutrient in the ocean is:
    a. silicon
    b. oxygen
    c. nitrogen
    d. carbonate
    e. phosphorus
22. Where is primary production the least?
    a. coasts
    b. upwelling along coasts
    c. gyres
    d. around Antarctica in the summer
    e. along Equator

23. The fall bloom in temperate waters is caused when:
    a. primary production decreases as nutrients increase
    b. primary production decreases due to light limitation
    c. primary production decreases as nutrients decrease
    d. primary production increases as nutrients increase
    e. primary production increases as the number of zooplankton increases
24. Equatorial upwelling occurs as a result of:
    a. temperature changes at the Equator
    b. the divergence of equatorial surface currents
    c. the convergence of equatorial surface currents
    d. winds causing the Ekman transport of surface water offshore
    e. El Niño conditions north and south of the Equator
25. The Southern Oscillation can be described as:
    a. relative changes between two pressure systems
    b. variation in wind speed over the Pacific Ocean
    c. relationship between sea-surface and high-altitude pressures
    d. tidal differences between the Indian and Pacific Oceans
    e. wind-speed differences along the Equator

CHAPTER 15
THE OCEAN DEPTHS

1. The mesopelagic zone refers to the ocean depths in which there is:
    a. enough light to support plant growth
    b. no light at all
    c. dim light, but not enough for plant growth
    d. enough light for primary production by bacteria
    e. dim light, but enough to support only some hardy plants

2. In addition to food, deep-water animals depend on the surface for:
    a. light
    b. carbon dioxide
    c. chlorophyll
    d. oxygen
    e. all of the above

3. The mesopelagic zone extends from about 200 m to about:
    a. 300 m
    b. 500 m
    c. 1,000 m
    d. 2,000 m
    e. 4,000 m

4. The main thermocline is located:
    a. in the mesopelagic
    b. above the mesopelagic
    c. below the mesopelagic
    d. it varies since the thermocline disappears in the tropics
    e. it varies since the thermocline moves up and down in the water column depending on the amount of oxygen

5. Photophores are:
    a. specialized eyes
    b. buoyancy-regulating organs
    c. specialized jaws
    d. light-sensitive organs that lack the lens of true eyes
    e. light-producing organs

6. Common adaptations of mesopelagic fishes include all of the following except:
    a. large mouths
    b. large size
    c. extensible jaws
    d. needle-like teeth
    e. unspecialized diets

7. Non-vertical migrating mesopelagic fishes are characterized by having:
    a. large swim bladders
    b. strong, well-developed muscles
    c. well-developed bones
    d. large eyes
    e. large size

8. The deep-scattering layer (DSL) is a sound-reflecting layer that consists of:
   a. non-migrating fishes
   b. eipelagic fishes
   c. surface plankton
   d. phytoplankton
   e. migrating fishes
9. The tubular eyes of some midwater animals are adapted for:
   a. increasing the field of vision
   b. producing light
   c. seeing in the complete absence of light
   d. sensing changes in depth
   e. sensing changes in salinity
10. The presence of bioluminescent organs on the underside of midwater fishes is involved in:
    a. countershading
    b. enlargement of silhouette
    c. creating a transparency effect
    d. cryptic coloration
    e. counterillumination
11. Bioluminescence is used by midwater animals in all of these <u>except</u> in:
    a. communication
    b. warning coloration
    c. attracting prey
    d. counterillumination
    e. escaping from predators
12. The water below the oxygen minimum layer has:
    a. no oxygen at all
    b. only very small traces of oxygen
    c. some of the oxygen it had when it left the surface
    d. most of the oxygen it had when it left the surface
    e. all of the oxygen it had when it left the surface
13. The pelagic animals living in the waters of the ocean trenches is included in one of these zones:
    a. bathypelagic
    b. hadal pelagic
    c. abyssopelagic
    d. mesopelagic
    e. lower epipelagic
14. The zone immediately below the bathyal zone is called the:
    a. abyssal
    b. hadal
    c. subtidal
    d. subbathyal
    e. mesopelagic
15. Deep-sea pelagic fishes are characterized by all of the following <u>except</u>:
    a. small eyes
    b. absent or reduced swim bladder
    c. color spotted with red
    d. flabby muscles
    e. large mouth and teeth

16. An important feeding adaptation among deep-sea fishes:
    a. migration to shallower water to feed
    b. feeding on males, hence the term "male parasitism"
    c. ability to eat prey bigger than themselves
    d. strong muscles that allow them to move fast to catch any available prey
    e. absence of a stomach
17. Pheromones are special chemicals that are used to:
    a. digest food
    b. attract mates
    c. catch prey
    d. transport oxygen
    e. produce bioluminescence
18. The deep-sea benthos consists mostly of:
    a. deposit feeders
    b. filter feeders
    c. herbivores
    d. omnivores
    e. carnivores
19. The deep-sea scavengers include animals that feed on:
    a. deep-sea plankton
    b. bottom meiofauna
    c. particulate organic matter
    d. dead animals
    e. bacteria
20. The "experimental lunch" that was left on the *Alvin* as it rested on the bottom revealed that deep-sea bacteria:
    a. do not exist at all
    b. may cause diseases in humans exposed to them
    c. break down organic matter faster than in shallow water as a result of high pressure
    d. grow slower than shallow-water species
    e. are identical to those found in shallow water
21. The energy source for the bacteria that thrive around deep-sea hydrothermal vents is:
    a. hydrogen sulfide
    b. light
    c. heat from the hydrothermal vents
    d. detritus
    e. tube worm tissues
22. Bacteria thriving around deep-sea hydrothermal vents are:
    a. photosynthethic
    b. symbiotic
    c. heterotrophic
    d. parasitic
    e. chemiosynthetic
23. The giant deep-sea hydrothermal vent tube worm feeds on:
    a. plankton
    b. detritus
    c. small bottom animals such as brittle stars
    d. deep-sea bottom fishes
    e. none of the above: the worm does not have a mouth

24. The major advantage that deep-sea benthic animals have over pelagic ones is that their food:
    a. is easier to digest
    b. falls to the bottom and stays in one place, thus being available for a longer time
    c. gets to be eaten before it gets to pelagic animals
    d. gets less decayed by bacteria
    e. produces less detritus
25. A shrimp that occurs in large numbers around deep-sea hydrothermal vents does not have eyes. Light-sensitive cells on the top of the body, however, appear to be used to detect faint light from:
    a. bioluminescent predators
    b. the surface
    c. faint glow around vents
    d. bioluminescent prey
    e. mates

CHAPTER 16
RESOURCES FROM THE SEA

1. Finfish and shellfish provide approximately what percentage of animal protein consumed by humans around the world?
    a. 0.5%
    b. 1%
    c. 10%
    d. 20%
    e. 30%

2. Traditional fisheries are those that:
    a. catches are routinely recorded
    b. catch shellfish, not finfish
    c. do not use boats
    d. use relatively simple gear and methods
    e. catches are not sold to the general public

3. When did the world population reach 5 billion?
    a. not yet: it is expected to reach 5 billion by 2000
    b. not yet: it is expected to reach 5 billion by 2020
    c. 1995
    d. 1990
    e. late 1980s

4. One nation where annual catches have <u>not</u> decreased since the late 1980s:
    a. Japan
    b. Russia
    c. United States
    d. China
    e. Canada

5. Most marine food resources are taken from:
    a. coral reefs
    b. the continental shelf
    c. open waters off the continental shelf
    d. estuaries
    e. mariculture ponds

6. The largest fish catches are those of:
    a. tunas
    b. herrings, sardines, and other clupeoid fishes
    c. cod, haddocks, related fishes
    d. salmon
    e. sharks, rays, and skates

7. By definition, demersal catches are those that are harvested from:
    a. the open water
    b. the bottom
    c. estuaries
    d. waters where primary production is increased by upwelling
    e. the continental shelf

8. By definition, pelagic catches are those that are harvested from:
   a. the open water
   b. the bottom
   c. estuaries
   d. waters where primary production is increased by upwelling
   e. the continental shelf
9. Clupeoid fishes:
   a. feed on small fishes
   b. are demersal fishes
   c. live in the deep sea and migrate to the surface at night
   d. are caught exclusively for industrial purposes
   e. feed on plankton and typically form huge schools
10. The major fishing areas of the world are mostly located in waters:
   a. where coral reefs are common
   b. where equatorial upwelling takes place
   c. in open waters far from coasts
   d. where coastal upwelling takes place
   e. around Antarctica and in the Arctic
11. The major fishing area in the world is in the:
   a. northwest Pacific
   b. waters around Antarctica
   c. west Indian Ocean
   d. southwest Atlantic
   e. Mediterranean
12. Trawls are nets that:
   a. surround and trap fish
   b. float on the surface
   c. are allowed to drift along the surface
   d. placed along the bottom to trap passing fishes
   e. dragged along the bottom or through the water column
13. Industrial fisheries employ the catch for all of the following purposes except one:
   a. fish meal
   b. fish oil
   c. food
   d. poultry food
   e. fertilizers
14. An example of a marine non-renewable resource:
   a. shellfish
   b. finfish
   c. oil
   d. seaweeds
   e. whales
15. The maximum sustainable yield is best defined as the:
   a. highest catch that can be taken without overfishing
   b. maximum fishing effort allowed after overfishing is reached
   c. highest catch that will pay the minimum cost of the fishing effort
   d. minimum catch that will still allow the population to grow
   e. the annual size of the catch that will balance natural death and predation

16. Continued catches above the maximum sustainable yield:
    a. can be increased to prevent overfishing
    b. will result in underutilization
    c. will result in a decrease of fishing effort
    d. must be decreased in order to decrease population size
    e. will result in overfishing
17. Fishing effort refers to all of the following except:
    a. number of fishing boats
    b. number of fishermen
    c. number and size of fishing nets
    d. amount of time spent at sea
    e. size of the catch
18. One of the following best describes commercial fisheries around the world:
    a. most have been affected by overfishing
    b. about 20% have been affected by overfishing
    c. all have been affected by overfishing
    d. all have been affected by overfishing but none have been exhausted
    e. none have been affected by overfishing in the Southern Hemisphere
19. Fisheries management involves all of the following except:
    a. determining the optimal catch of a fish population
    b. determining when female fish begin releasing eggs
    c. limiting the size and sex of the fish caught
    d. restricting the number of fishing boats
    e. determining the fishing gear that can be used
20. The exclusive economic zone (EEZ) of a nation is equal to how many nautical miles:
    a. 10
    b. 20
    c. 100
    d. 200
    e. 1,000
21. Most of the krill fished for commercial purposes is caught in:
    a. Alaska
    b. Russia
    c. Antarctica
    d. the Arctic Ocean
    e. the North Sea
22. The "by-catch" is the name given to:
    a. junk species that are caught while fishing for more valuable species
    b. species caught for industrial purposes
    c. krill and other shellfish
    d. species raised in fish farms
    e. species caught as part of traditional fisheries
23. The type of mariculture that takes place under more or less natural conditions with little manipulation by humans is known as:
    a. traditional mariculture
    b. aquaculture
    c. closed intensive mariculture
    d. open mariculture
    e. industrial mariculture

24. Seeding in mariculture refers to:
    a. feeding fry with food raised in land farms
    b. enriching natural populations by releasing fish that have been farmed for a short time
    c. removing diseased fishes
    d. the culture of shellfish on racks or baskets
    e. the farming of fish in open mariculture

25. By the year 2000 farmed fish will account for approximately what percentage of the total world consumption?
    a. 1%
    b. 2%
    c. 10%
    d. 20%
    c. 100%

26. Releasing farmed salmon fry to grow at sea and harvesting them when they return to the river where they were released is called:
    a. open mariculture
    b. closed mariculture
    c. salmon ranching
    d. traditional salmon runs
    e. intensive mariculture

27. Offshore oil is drilled mostly from:
    a. deep sea
    b. coral reefs
    c. estuaries
    d. continental shelf
    e. mid-ocean ridge

28. Other than manganese, manganese nodules contain:
    a. nickel
    b. gold
    c. coal
    d. oil
    e. silver

29. Desalination plants:
    a. extract minerals for industrial use from seawater
    b. convert seawater into fresh water
    c. extract table salt from seawater
    d. convert seawater into brackish water for industrial uses
    e. extract oil from seawater

30. Potential sources of energy that can be obtained from the sea include all of the following except;
    a. tides
    b. waves
    c. currents
    d. differences in temperature between deep and shallow water
    e. manganese nodules

CHAPTER 17
IMPACT OF HUMANS ON THE MARINE ENVIRONMENT

1. Pollution is best described as:
    a. adding substances or energy that harm the environment
    b. changing the population growth of species
    c. the decrease in the quality of the environment as a result of natural events
    d. substances or materials that are toxic to humans
    e. decreasing the quality of the human environment

2. The two most important sources of oil pollution in the marine environment are:
    a. tanker and blowout accidents
    b. tar balls and tanker accidents
    c. natural seepage and urban runoff
    d. urban wastes and normal operation of tankers
    e. blowout accidents and urban wastes

3. The most harmful oil spills in terms of damage to the marine environment are generally considered to be:
    a. blowout of offshore rigs
    b. discharge of oil during the unloading of tankers
    c. sinking or collision of tankers
    d. runoff from coastal cities
    e. natural seepage

4. A substance that is biodegradable:
    a. evaporates very slowly
    b. forms tar balls or other solid residues
    c. can be broken down only by special chemicals
    d. sinks to the bottom
    e. can be broken down by bacteria

5. After oil spills, what type of marine animals are most likely to die of exposure?
    a. migrating fishes like salmon
    b. cetaceans
    c. sea urchins
    d. filter-feeding fishes
    e. seabirds

6. People sometimes contract hepatitis from eating raw shellfish because the shellfish:
    a. are the normal carrier of the hepatitis virus
    b. keep alive the virus in the water kept within the shell
    c. filter the virus from sewage-contamined water
    d. keep the virus alive in its nervous system
    e. are most likely spoiled

7. Sludge is best defined as:
    a. raw sewage
    b. semiliquid material that results from sewage treatment
    c. industrial sewage
    d. water removed during sewage treatment
    e. decay bacteria in sewage

8. Accumulation of sludge on the bottom of the ocean is responsible for:
   a. anaerobic, or oxygen-lacking conditions
   b. drastic changes in salinity
   c. deposit feeders being replaced by filter feeders
   d. drastic changes in temperature
   e. increase in the number of sharks and other predators
9. Eutrophication is a type of pollution caused by:
   a. pesticides
   b. oil runoff
   c. high-temperature water
   d. fertilizers
   e. radioactive material
10. Chlorinated hydrocarbons are found most commonly in:
    a. fertilizers
    b. sewage
    c. oil
    d. aerosol containers
    e. pesticides
11. A persistent chemical is one that is:
    a. toxic
    b. non-biodegradable
    c. a thermal pollutant
    d. insoluble in water
    e. resistant to detergents
12. Persistent chemicals are particularly harmful to the environment because they:
    a. are toxic to plants and other autotrophs
    b. are not soluble in seawater
    c. interfere with the oxygen intake of organisms
    d. are toxic since they are radioactive
    e. accumulate in organisms that are higher in the food chain
13. A type of seabird that was particularly affected by pesticides such as DDT:
    a. pelicans
    b. cormorants
    c. common gulls
    d. frigate birds
    e. herons
14. Which of the following organisms are expected to show the highest concentration of DDT and other chlorinated hydrocarbons in its tissues?
    a. filter-feeding fishes
    b. carnivorous fishes
    c. phytoplankton
    d. sea lions
    e. zooplankton
15. Chlorinated hydrocarbons reach the marine environment by way of:
    a. fertilizers used in farms along the shore
    b. thermal pollution
    c. land-nesting seabirds
    d. river runoff
    e. underwater volcanic eruptions

16. PCBs are characterized by being:
    a. persistent
    b. easily biodegradable
    c. radioactive
    d. responsible for global warming
    e. eutrophication
17. One of the following has been implicated in abnormal sexual behavior in seabirds:
    a. sewage pollution
    b. chlorinated hydrocarbons
    c. thermal pollution
    d. heavy metals
    e. eutrophication
18. Heavy metals include all of the following except:
    a. lead
    b. PCBs
    c. mercury
    d. cadmium
    e. copper
19. Mercury has been directly linked with one of the following health problems in humans:
    a. hepatitis
    b. cancer
    c. neurological disorders and paralysis
    d. digestive disorders
    e. respiratory problems
20. One of the following is known to be responsible for thermal pollution:
    a. radioactive fallout
    b. sewage
    c. excessive use of fertilizers
    d. solid waste
    e. power plants
21. The loss of estuaries and mangrove forests is particularly serious since these ecosystems:
    a. provide nesting or resting areas to many seabirds
    b. are among the most productive of all marine ecosystems
    c. provide habitats to many species
    d. directly or indirectly provide food to many species
    e. all of the above are true
22. Coral reefs are being directly affected by the destruction of:
    a. tropical rain forests
    b. estuaries
    c. sandy beaches
    d. salt marshes
    e. mud flats
23. A threatened species is one that is:
    a. in immediate danger of extinction
    b. at risk of extinction since its members are low in number
    c. not at risk even if its members are low in number
    d. at great risk since it only exists in zoos or marine parks
    e. within a few years of disappearing forever

24. The Steller sea cow was brought to extinction by:
    a. the destruction of kelp beds
    b. the occupation of land by whalers
    c. whalers hunting for meat
    d. the filling in of estuaries
    e. increase in sediments in the water brought about by the cutting of nearby forests
25. The primary reason why the great whales occur now in such low numbers is intensive whaling plus:
    a. their low reproductive potential
    b. the fact that they migrate, thus getting exposed to more whalers
    c. the necessity of having to surface to breathe
    d. their habit of remaining together in schools
    e. their habit of migrating to Antarctica
26. The first whale to be seriously depleted was the:
    a. fin
    b. minke
    c. blue
    d. right
    e. gray
27. A whale no longer included among the endangered species:
    a. fin
    b. minke
    c. blue
    d. right
    e. gray
28. Protection of whales by the International Whaling Commission (IWC) is ineffective due to the fact that its quotas:
    a. do not apply to Japan
    b. do not apply to all of the great whales
    c. are applicable only to the United States and Russia
    d. are non-binding, thus may be rejected by a nation
    e. are applicable only to blue and minke whales
29. Alien species are known to be transported into a new location by way of:
    a. ocean currents
    b. plankton brought in by currents
    c. transplanted oysters
    d. natural migration
    e. young individuals brought in by currents
30. Sustainable development refers to development that:
    a. remains stable year after year
    b. safeguards natural resources for future generations of people
    c. does not alter ocean currents, salinity or any other physical or chemical factors in the environment
    d. does not significantly affect the growth of wildlife
    e. changes depending on the importance given by future generations of the use of particular resources

CHAPTER 18
THE OCEANS AND HUMAN AFFAIRS

1. The oceans are said to have served as barriers of culture as a result of:
   a. protection by most nations of their seaports
   b. banning of ocean-going commerce until the sixteenth century
   c. stiff import-export trade barriers
   d. belief in the western world that the earth was flat
   e. lack of maps

2. A group of people that are known to have carried out long voyages of discovery across the ocean before the Europeans:
   a. Polynesians
   b. native Americans
   c. Eskimos
   d. South American Indians
   e. native Californian tribes

3. In the fifteenth century, the nation that pioneered the discovery of new lands by crossing the oceans:
   a. Italy
   b. China
   c. Portugal
   d. Russia
   e. England

4. Who first landed in America from Europe?
   a. Spaniards
   b. Englishmen
   c. Italians
   d. Russians
   e. Vikings

5. In terms of total volume, seaborne trade is dominated by:
   a. crude oil
   b. fruits and vegetables
   c. coffee
   d. sugar
   e. pharmaceuticals

6. In the native cultures of this region salmon and killer whales provide a source of many legends and religious beliefs:
   a. Australia
   b. northern Europe
   c. South Africa
   d. Caribbean
   e. Pacific Northwest

7. Cultures that have evolved in close contact with the marine environment are known by anthropologists as:
   a. maritime
   b. oceanic
   c. seaborne
   d. marine
   e. neritic

8. A native culture that uses eelgrass as an important resource can be found in:
   a. Polynesia
   b. Gulf of California
   c. Falkland Islands
   d. Japan
   e. India

9. The livelihood of the Hanseatic League of northern Europe was based on what particular fishery?
   a. herring
   b. salmon
   c. freshwater eel
   d. cod
   e. tuna

10. Some unique cultures that have been very much influenced by the sea exist in isolated areas where the economy is still based on:
    a. tourism
    b. interocean transportation
    c. fishing
    d. handicrafts
    e. international trade

11. Perhaps the most remarkable example of reclamation of land from the sea bottom is found in:
    a. France
    b. China
    c. Italy
    d. the Netherlands
    e. Norway

12. Ecotourism combines travel and:
    a. business in the exploitation of fish resources
    b. visit to areas of natural interest
    c. visit to areas of artistic interest
    d. visit to areas of archeological
    e. the aquarium trade

13. As far as the transit through sea straits that fall within the jurisdiction of more than one nation, the United Nations Conference on the Law of the Sea stipulates that control falls:
    a. on the largest nation
    b. on the nation having the longest coastline along the particular strait
    c. on international waters
    d. on both nations at the same time
    e. on the nations belonging to the U.N. Security Council

14. The territorial sea of a nation is defined as the water between a nation's coastline to a distance of how many nautical miles?
    a. 1
    b. 2
    c. 3
    d. 12
    e. 100

15. The exclusive economic zone (EEZ) defines the interests that a nation may have over what type of activities?
    a. defense
    b. commerce
    c. tourism
    d. nuclear testing
    e. oil exploitation

ANSWERS:

CHAPTER 1
1. a
2. d
3. c
4. d
5. e
6. d
7. b
8. e
9. b
10. a
11. c
12. c
13. b
14. a
15. e

CHAPTER 2
1. d
2. b
3. e
4. a
5. a
6. c
7. b
8. b
9. c
10. e
11. b
12. d
13. e
14. d
15. a
16. a
17. b
18. d
19. d
20. a
21. b
22. e
23. c
24. e
25. d

CHAPTER 3
1. c
2. d
3. a

4. b
5. c
6. b
7. d
8. e
9. e
10. a
11. b
12. e
13. a
14. d
15. c
16. c
17. a
18. b
19. e
20. e
21. d
22. c
23. d
24. a
25. b

CHAPTER 4
1. b
2. a
3. d
4. d
5. c
6. e
7. c
8. a
9. d
10. e
11. c
12. b
13. b
14. e
15. a
16. d
17. a
18. a
19. d
20. b
21. c
22. b
23. c
24. b

25. d

CHAPTER 5
1. d
2. b
3. e
4. e
5. c
6. d
7. a
8. b
9. c
10. c
11. a
12. e
13. b
14. a
15. a
16. c
17. b
18. d
19. d
20. e
21. b
22. d
23. c
24. b
25. e

CHAPTER 6
1. b
2. a
3. e
4. b
5. c
6. d
7. e
8. c
9. a
10. c
11. d
12. e
13. b
14. a
15. a
16. d
17. b
18. e

19. b
20. c
21. d
22. c
23. b
24. a
25. e
26. d
27. b
28. a
29. d
30. d

CHAPTER 7
1. b
2. b
3. c
4. a
5. a
6. e
7. e
8. d
9. c
10. d
11. b
12. c
13. b
14. a
15. d
16. c
17. e
18. b
19. e
20. a
21. a
22. c
23. c
24. e
25. d
26. b
27. c
28. a
29. e
30. d

CHAPTER 8
1. a
2. c

3. d
4. c
5. e
6. b
7. c
8. e
9. a
10. a
11. a
12. d
13. c
14. b
15. b
16. a
17. b
18. d
19. e
20. e
21. d
22. b
23. c
24. e
25. a
26. c
27. d
28. b
29. d
30. d

CHAPTER 9
1. b
2. b
3. e
4. e
5. a
6. c
7. d
8. d
9. a
10. c
11. b
12. e
13. d
14. c
15. d
16. e
17. a
18. a

19. d
20. b
21. c
22. e
23. b
24. a
25. c

CHAPTER 10
1. c
2. c
3. a
4. e
5. b
6. d
7. d
8. e
9. a
10. b
11. c
12. a
13. b
14. b
15. e
16. d
17. c
18. e
19. a
20. b
21. c
22. a
23. d
24. d
25. b

CHAPTER 11
1. b
2. c
3. e
4. e
5. a
6. c
7. a
8. b
9. d
10. d
11. e
12. b
13. a

14. a
15. d
16. c
17. e
18. e
19. b
20. c
21. c
22. c
23. d
24. a
25. d

CHAPTER 12
1. b
2. a
3. c
4. c
5. d
6. b
7. e
8. a
9. c
10. e
11. d
12. d
13. a
14. e
15. e
16. b
17. c
18. d
19. a
20. b
21. e
22. a
23. c
24. d
25. b

CHAPTER 13
1. e
2. d
3. d
4. e
5. a
6. b
7. d
8. c

9. b
10. c
11. a
12. e
13. d
14. c
15. b
16. e
17. a
18. a
19. a
20. c
21. b
22. d
23. b
24. c
25. e

CHAPTER 14
1. b
2. c
3. a
4. b
5. d
6. e
7. b
8. a
9. c
10. e
11. b
12. d
13. c
14. e
15. e
16. d
17. e
18. d
19. a
20. a
21. c
22. c
23. d
24. b
25. a

CHAPTER 15
1. c
2. d
3. c

4. a
5. e
6. b
7. d
8. e
9. a
10. e
11. b
12. d
13. b
14. a
15. c
16. c
17. b
18. a
19. d
20. d
21. e
22. e
23. e
24. b
25. c

CHAPTER 16
1. c
2. d
3. e
4. d
5. b
6. b
7. b
8. a
9. e
10. d
11. a
12. e
13. c
14. c
15. a
16. e
17. e
18. a
19. b
20. d
21. c
22. a
23. d
24. b
25. c

26. c
27. d
28. a
29. b
30. e

CHAPTER 17
1. a
2. d
3. c
4. e
5. e
6. c
7. b
8. a
9. d
10. e
11. b
12. e
13. a
14. d
15. d
16. a
17. b
18. b
19. c
20. e
21. e
22. a
23. c
24. c
25. a
26. d
27. e
28. d
29. c
30. b

CHAPTER 18
1. d
2. a
3. c
4. e
5. a
6. e
7. a
8. b
9. a
10. c